C000151662

THE
ANFIELD
SONGBOOK

WE HAVE DREAMS AND SONGS TO SING

THE
ANFIELD
SONGBOOK

WE HAVE DREAMS AND SONGS TO SING

  WESTERN UNION **WU** BETVICTOR

Trinity Mirror Sport Media

Copyright © Liverpool Football Club

*The right of Liverpool Football Club to be identified as the owner of this
work has been asserted in accordance with the Copyright, Designs and
Patents Act, 1988.*

*All Rights Reserved. No part of this publication may be reproduced,
stored in a retrieval system, or transmitted in any form, or by any means,
electronic, mechanical, photocopying, recording or otherwise without
the prior permission in writing of the copyright holders, nor be otherwise
circulated in any form of binding or cover other than in which it is published
and without a similar condition being imposed on the subsequent publisher.*

2017 Updated edition

First published in Great Britain in 2010.
Reprinted in 2011 and 2012. Updated and reprinted in 2017 by
Trinity Mirror Sport Media,
PO Box 48, Old Hall Street, Liverpool L69 3EB.

www.tmsportmedia.com
@SportMediaTM

Trinity Mirror Sport Media is a part of Trinity Mirror plc.
One Canada Square, Canary Wharf, London, E15 5AP.

Updated edition ISBN: 978-1-910335-63-5
Original ISBN: 978-1-906802-44-8

Photographic acknowledgements:
Liverpool FC Getty Images, PA.

Production and Editing: Michael McGuinness
Writer: Chris McLoughlin

Printed and bound by CPI Group (UK) Ltd, Croydon, CR0 4YY.

We're A Happy Band...

tood shoulder to shoulder, scarves held aloft, the images of Liverpool FC supporters singing You'll Never Walk Alone before a game at Anfield are some of the most famous in football.

Wherever you are in the world, if you hear that song you think of Liverpool Football Club, of Anfield, of the Kop in full voice.

Rodgers and Hammerstein may have wrote it, and Gerry Marsden took it to number one in the charts, but it is the supporters of Liverpool FC who have made it world famous.

It is Anfield's anthem. The motto on our badge. A Kopite's calling card. A song sung with passion, desire, defiance and emotion.

But You'll Never Walk Alone is far from the only song to pass from the collective lips of Liverpool FC supporters. It is simply the most famous of hundreds of songs and chants that have passed through the collective lips of Liverpudlians over the years.

That singing culture has played a significant part in creating Anfield's unique aura and making the Kop the most famous stand in football.

Collective chanting and singing at football matches is taken for granted now, but before the early 1960s that wasn't the case.

It all changed at Anfield in 1963/64. With The Beatles taking the Mersey Sound around the world and Bill Shankly's Redmen en-route to winning the league, those on the Kop wanted to shout about it.

So they did, en-masse, with up to 28,000 singing and swaying along to whatever was played over the PA System before kick-off.

It was communal karaoke, the like of which had never been seen before in English football, with the natural Scouse wit soon lending itself to adapting the words to well known tunes to express admiration for their heroes and distain for opponents.

And so the sound of Anfield resonated around the world and the Liverpool FC songbook began.

The partisan vocal backing our players have received during the course of our history has been a significant factor in bringing so much success to LFC. The Anfield Songbook is a tribute to that magnificent support.

We have compiled hundreds of songs and chants that have been written and sung by Liverpool FC supporters over the years and included as many as we can in this updated 2017 songbook – although there are several we simply can't publish!

Many have been aired at Anfield, others only on away trips. Some have never been heard outside of pubs and bars, a few have been posted by creative Reds on Liverpool FC message boards while others have gone viral on YouTube, Twitter and Facebook.

Our collection is not definitive – no LFC songbook ever could be – and the words to certain tunes have varied, been changed and updated over the years, but The Anfield

Songbook gives a taste of the unique, inventive, humourous and inspirational songs that have been sung by Liverpool FC supporters all round the fields of Anfield Road.

You never walk alone when you're a Kopite. You never sing alone either.

" There's not one club in Europe with an anthem like You'll Never Walk Alone. There's not one club in the world so united with the fans. I sat there watching the Liverpool fans and they sent shivers down my spine. A mass of 40,000 people became one force behind their team. That's something not many teams have. For that I admire Liverpool more than anything "

Johan Cruyff

The songs in this book are those sung
by the supporters of Liverpool FC and do
not necessarily represent the position of
Liverpool Football Club

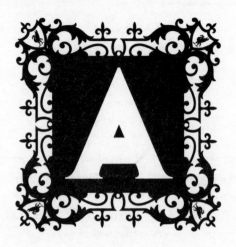

A Cat

A cat, a cat, a cat a cat a cat...

(Kopites have long sung 'attack, attack, attack attack attack' to urge Liverpool FC to push forward but in February 2012 they wittily adapted the chant when a feline pitch invader – since nicknamed 'The Anfield Cat' – ran on during a game against Tottenham Hotspur)

A Little Touch Of Scotland

A little touch of Scotland came to Liverpool one day,
He looked around and said:
"Och man aye, this is where I'll stay,"
And from that moment he worked hard
to build a team so grand,
And now today we have the greatest
team in all the land.

[Chorus]:
Shankly, oh yes Bill Shankly,
Shankly we love you,
For all the things you've done for us
while here at Liverpool,
Bill Shankly we thank you.

Nowhere would you find a man who is the same as he,
And all who meet him love him for his humility,
For that and many other things our thanks we give to him,
And do you see we're talking of Bill Shankly,
Aye that's him!

[Chorus]:
Shankly, oh yes Bill Shankly,
Shankly we love you.
For all the things you've done for us while here at Liverpool,
Bill Shankly we thank you.

A-B-L, E-T-T
(To the tune of 'Jesus Christ Superstar')

A-B-L *[clap clap]*,
E-T-T *[clap clap]*,
Gary Ablett is the one for me.

(Originally the song for Albert Stubbins, this was revived for Gary Ablett in the 1980s but got its best airing of all at Villa Park in 1994 when news filtered through from Goodison Park that Ablett, then playing for Everton, had scored an own goal against Wimbledon that looked to be sending the Blues down)

After The Ball Is Over

After the game is over,
After the whistle blew,
Campbell got excited,
And down the wing he flew.

He passed the ball to Liddell,
Liddell scored a goal,
And left poor Everton's goalie,
Flying on his 'ole.

*(Adapted from 'After The Ball' – written by American songwriter
Charles K Harris in 1891 – a song about an old man recounting the
story of his long-lost love to his niece)*

Agger Doo
(To the tune 'Agadoo' by Black Lace)

Agger doo, doo, doo,
Plays with Carra or Sami,
Agger doo, doo, doo,
Plays for Liverpool FC.

He can shoot,
He can score,
From thirty yards like Stevie G.
Agger doo, doo, doo,
Plays for Liverpool FC.

Agger doo, doo, doo,
Since we signed him from Brondby,
Agger doo, doo, doo,
Plays for Liverpool FC.

To the left, to the right,
He brings strikers to their knees.
Agger doo, doo, doo,
Plays for Liverpool FC.

Alan Hansen
(To the tune of 'Na Na Hey Hey Kiss Him Goodbye' by Bananarama)

Na na nah na. Na na na na,
Hey hey, Alan Hansen!

A-L-B, E-R-T

You can keep Billy Liddell,
You can keep Roger Hunt,
David Johnson was a bit of a ****.
You can keep Kenny Dalglish,
You can keep Ian Rush,
Albert Stubbins is the man for us.
A-L-B *[clap clap]*,
E-R-T *[clap clap]*,
Albert Stubbins is the one for me.

*(One of the earliest player songs in honour of an Anfield
goalscoring legend, although not aired until after his retirement)*

Alberto Moreno

(To the tune of 'La Bamba' by Los Lobos)

Albert Albert Moreno,

Albert Albert Moreno,

From Sevilla and Manquillo (and Manquillo!)

Albert Moreno, Albert Moreno...

(Vine footage of this impromptu song breaking out on a coach full of Reds on the way back from a game at Tottenham did the rounds on social media in 2014 although Alberto Moreno lost an 'o' from his name to make the words fit!)

Allez Allez

Allez allez, *(Allez allez),*

Allez allez, *(Allez allez),*

Gerard Houllier,

Allez allez, *(Allez allez),*

Allez allez, *(Allez allez),*

Gerard Houllier.

(A popular chant during the reign of the Frenchman and can be traced back to Boavista in 2001, where 500 travelling Reds started the tune during half-time of a Champions League tie)

A-L-O-N-S-O
(To the tune of The Beatles' 'Ob-La-Di Ob-La-Da')

[Chorus]:
A-L-O-N-S-O, it's Alonso, Xabi, Xabi Alonso,
A-L-O-N-S-O, it's Alonso, Xabi, Xabi Alonso.

He came from Sociedad to play in our midfield,
His passing and his shooting are sublime,
If we had to choose between him and Fat Frank,
We would choose Xabi every time.

A-L-O-N-S-O, it's Alonso, Xabi, Xabi Alonso,
A-L-O-N-S-O, it's Alonso, Xabi, Xabi Alonso.

We drew Luton Town in the FA Cup,
Xabi and the keeper had a race,
Xabi had a shot from 70 yards,
You should have seen the look on Gerrard's face.
A-L-O-N-S-O, it's Alonso, Xabi, Xabi Alonso,
A-L-O-N-S-O, it's Alonso, Xabi, Xabi Alonso.

Alonso, Alonso, Alonso (I)
(To the tune of 'Let It Snow')

Oh he is a midfield maestro,
And his passing's so delightful,
Everyone wants to know,
Alonso, Alonso, Alonso.

Alonso, Alonso, Alonso (II)
(To the tune 'Mexican Hat')

Alonso, Alonso, Alonso,
Alonso, Alonso, Alonso,
Alonso, Alonso, Alonso,
Alonso, Alonso, Alonso!

(This was sung at a fast pace while jumping at the same time)

Anfield
(To the hymn 'Jerusalem' by Hubert Parry)

And did Shankly in ancient times,
Walk upon Anfield's pastures green,
And was our holy manager God,
To Europe's greatest football team.

And did Paisley surpass him still,
And bring back titles and cups at will,
And was the Spion Kop builded here,
Beneath the Liver Bird's bill.

Bring me Fagan and Tommy Smith,
Bring me Benitez's Spanish fire,
Bring me Gerrard! and Carragher!
The backbone of our team tonight.

We will not cease from mental fight,
Nor shall our swords sleep in our hands.
'Til we have won the cup for good,
And brought it back to Anfield again.

*(Although the music was written by Sir Hubert Parry in 1916, the words
came about from a short poem by William Blake in the early nineteenth
century. This song has never been sung at a Liverpool FC match but would
sound good if it was!)*

Anfield Rap (Red Machine In Full Effect)

Liverpool FC is hard as hell,
United, Tottenham, Arsenal,
Watch my lips and I will spell,
'Cos they don't just play,
But they can rap as well.

Liverpool FC,
Liverpool FC.

(My idea was to build Liverpool into a bastion of invincibility
you know like... aah...aah...aah...aah ...had Napoleon had
that idea he'd have conquered the bloody world)

[Chorus]:
Walk on...walk on...with hope...in your
heart...and you'll ne...ver walk...alone.

Alright Aldo,
Sound as a pound,
I'm cushty la but there's nothing down.

Anfield Rap

The official club anthem for the 1988 FA Cup final meeting with Wimbledon was Craig Johnston's idea, not John Barnes' as many think, and is a parody of a number of hip hop tracks. At the time, there were only two Scousers in the first team – John Aldridge and Steve McMahon – and the theme of the song revolves around their team-mates' strange accents. The Anfield Rap made it to number three in the UK charts, while the accompanying video has ensured it will live long in our memories with over 1.65m views on YouTube as of July 2017.

The rest of the lads ain't got it sussed,
We'll have to learn 'em to talk like us.

Well I'm rapping now, I'm rapping for fun,
I'm your goalie, your number one.
You can take the mick, don't call me a clown,
Any more lip and you're going down.

Ar ay ace, we're great me and you,
But the other lads don't talk like we do.
No they don't talk like we do, do they do la,
We'll have to learn 'em to talk propah.

*Walk on...walk on...with hope...in your heart...
and you'll ne...ver walk...alone.*

You two Scousers are always yapping,
I'm gonna show you some serious rapping.
I come from Jamaica, my name is John Barn-es,
When I do my thing the crowd go bananas.

How's he doing the Jamaica rap?
He's from just south of the Watford Gap.
He gives us stick about the north/south divide,
'Cos they got the jobs,
Yeah, but we got the side.

Well I came to England looking for fame,
So come on Kenny man, give us a game,
'Cos I'm sat on the bench paying my dues and my fees,
I'm very big down under, but my wife disagrees.

We Have Dreams And Songs To Sing

They've won the league, bigger stars than Dallas,
They've got more silver than Buckingham Palace.
No-one knows quite what to expect,
When the red machine's in full effect.

Well Steve McMahon sure can rap,
It's about time he had an England cap.
So come on Bobby Robson, he's the man,
'Cause if anyone can, Macca can...
Macca can...Macca can...Macca can...Macca can...

Liverpool FC is hard as hell.
(My idea was to build Liverpool up and up and up until
eventually they would be untouchable. Everybody would
have to submit. Give in, give in, give in)

We're Highland lads,
Och-ay the noo,
And there's four of us,
And only two of you.
So if you want nai trouble,
And you don't want a slap,
You'd better teach us the Anfield Rap.

Don't forget us paddies,
And me the Great Dane,
And I'm from London mate, so watch your game.
Well you two Scousers, you're always squawking,
But we'll just let our feet do the talking.

Our lads have come from all over the place,
They talk dead funny, but they play dead great.

Well know we've gotta learn 'em to talk real cool,
The song you've gotta learn if you live in the 'pool.

Walk on…walk on…with hope…in your heart…
and you'll ne…ver walk…alone.
You'll ne-ver walk a-lone.

Ho-ho my word,
That's unbelievable, it really is.
I think they should stick to playing football.
Terrible. What do you think Kenny?
Oh yeah!

Anfield Way

Down Anfield Way the world is gay,
All Kopites are to tingle,
With rows and rows of crimson flags,
From Bootle up to Dingle.
The toast is to eleven men,
Who wear the scarlet jersey,
Their names will live forever more,
Along the river Mersey.

They'll take their place in history,
Amongst the all-time greats,
Thompson, Byrne, St John, and Hunt,
And Skipper Rowdy Yeats.
So let us sing a song or two,
On Wembley's famous ground,

And let London town re-echo,
To that famous Mersey sound.

They beat the Leeds two goals to one,
And Rowdy met the queen,
And Gerry broke his collar bone,
As brave as you have seen.
And when they bring that cup back home,
Through streets all paved in Red,
Those Liver Birds will fly away,
Just like Bill Shankly said.

(Liverpool FC's first ever FA Cup winning team is immortalised in song after their 2-1 Wembley victory over Leeds United in 1965. The song, along with the joyous scenes which greeted the team on their return to Merseyside, suitably reflect the mood of the fans and the importance of that first FA Cup)

Anfield Wig Walk

I'm a knock-kneed chicken,
I'm bow-legged hen,
I haven't been so happy,
Since I don't know when.
I walk with a wiggle and talk with a squawk,
Doing the Anfield wig walk.

(This rather strange ditty comes from 'Tennessee Wig Walk', a UK No.4 hit for American country singer Bonnie Lou in 1954. It was adopted by several clubs and regularly heard on the terraces during the late '50s and early '60s. Liverpool FC supporters also sang a version that began "I was walking down Lime Street swinging a chain, when up popped a Cockney and asked me my name" to welcome London clubs to Anfield, but we can't print the rest of it!)

Arbeloa
(To the tune of 'From Me To You' by The Beatles)

Arbelo-oaaaaaaa,

Arbelo-oaaaaaaa,

If there's anything that you want,

If there's anything he can do,

Just give him the ball and he'll run through and score

a goal for Liverpool.

(Alvaro Arbeloa only scored twice for Liverpool FC but this song emerged before the European Cup final in Athens in 2007, a month after his first Reds goal at Reading)

Aye-aye Sami Hyypia
(To the tune of 'She'll Be Coming Round The Mountain')

Singin' aye-aye Sami Hyypia,

Singin' aye-aye Sami Hyypia,

Singin' aye-aye Sami,

Aye-aye Sami,

Aye-aye Sami Hyypia.

Benny Is A Dancer
(To the tune of Snap's 'Rhythm Is A Dancer')

Benny is a dancer,
Skipping past defenders,
Benayoun is everywhere!

(Sung by a small group of Reds in tribute to Yossi Benayoun during the Europa League quarter-final victory over Benfica in April 2010)

Best Midfield In The World
(To the tune of 'The Entertainer' by Scott Joplin)

Whoa-oh, whoa-oh, whoa-oh,
We've got the best midfield in the world,
Xabi Alonso, Momo Sissoko, Gerrard and
Mascherano-o-oh!

(This song emerged in 2007 when the Reds were on their way to Athens for the Champions League final. It was famously sung in Monastiraki, Athens, by hundreds of Kopites doing a conga on the night after Liverpool FC had lost the final to AC Milan with two YouTube videos of it receiving over half-a-million hits! A decade later the Kop revived it on the final day of the 2016/17 season during a 3-0 win against Middlesbrough following the news that Xabi Alonso was to retire)

Big Ron Yeats

Let me tell you of our football team,
Liverpool is the name.
We've won the league, we've won the cup,
We're the finest in the game.
We've got the greatest skipper any manager could employ,
Let's drink six crates to big Ron Yeats,
Bill Shankly's pride and joy.

(Also known as 'Bill Shankly's Pride And Joy', this song salutes the leadership of Big Rowdy Ron Yeats)

Bill Shankly From Glenbuck
(To the tune of 'Sean South From Garryowen' by the Wolfe Tones)

'Twas on a cold December's day,
Back in 1959,
When a man came down from Huddersfield Town,
To lead the Anfield line.
He bought Yeats from Dundee and St John,
And the football world was shook,
This man he became a legend,
Bill Shankly from Glenbuck.

On the Kop we'd sway and sing,
'Til our hearts would burst with pride,
And Shanks he made a pact with us,
To build another side.
With Keegan, Tosh and Steve Heighway,
The great man kept his word,
Then in '74 he bade farewell,
Our dear old Scottish Laird.

Now when Shanks was gone we sang 'Walk On'
But feared we'd walk alone,
The search was on to find the one,
Who could fill the master's throne.
The one we crowned became renowned,
Throughout the football game,
Three European Cups, six championships,
Bob Paisley was his name.

Now when Bob stepped down he left his crown,
Inside his Anfield home.
Joe Fagan came and brought new fame,
With a treble won in Rome.
Though the Heysel year left Joe in tears,
The following year he'd sing,
When we won the league and FA Cup,
And Kenny was our king.

When he played in red, Bob Paisley said,
He's the best he'd ever seen,
And the team he built in '88,
Ruled the football league supreme.
And when Hillsborough left us all bereaved,

And the Kop bedecked in flowers,
Kenny proved he truly was a king,
In Anfield's darkest hour.

Now the mantle's being passed to a man from France,
And it's Houllier we praise,
As the Reds walk on, the Kop's in song,
And we savour glory days.
Days of ball to feet, of victory sweet,
Days of passion, guile and fire,
The legacy of one so great,
Bill Shankly from Ayrshire.

(Penned by John Mackin, Kop season ticket holder since 1975, long-time fanzine writer, founder member of Reclaim The Kop and co-author of Redmen: A Season on The Drink)

Billy Liddell

(To the tune of Dean Martin's signature song 'That's Amore')

When he runs down the wing,
You can hear the Kop sing,
Billy Liddell!
When he runs through to score,
You can hear the Kop roar,
Billy Liddell.

La la la la la la, la la la la la la,
Bil-ly Lid-dell.

(The lyrics were also adapted for Djimi Traore, although they were used in less glowing terms – "When the ball hits his head and ends up in row Z it's Traore" being the sign-off line! The French-born Malian full-back is also the subject of another famous parody – see 'Blame It On Traore')

Billy The King

(To the tune of 'Lily The Pink' by The Scaffold)

Oh let's drink, a drink, a drink,
To Billy the king, the king, the king,
The creator of the greatest team,
For he invented professional football,
And this year we'll win the league.

Now Gerry Byrne,
Refused a tourniquet,
When he's broken his collar bone,
And they just rubbed on medicinal compound.
And Gerry goes marching on, on, ON!

Oh let's drink, a drink, a drink,
To Billy the king, the king, the king,
The creator of the greatest team,
For he invented professional football,
And this year we'll win the league.

(Another lyrical salute to Bill Shankly. 'Lily The Pink' is itself a parody of the folk song 'The Ballad Of Lydia Pinkham'. The Scaffold were a comedy, poetry and music trio from Liverpool FC consisting of Roger McGough, John Gorman and Mike McGear – brother of a little-known Paul McCartney!)

Biscan In Our Club

(To the theme tune from the Jacob's biscuits ad)

If you like Croatian players,
We've got Biscan in our club.

(Fondly recalled by children of the '80s, the Club biscuit bar advert turned into a latter day treat for one Anfield cult hero)

Bjornebye In My Gang

(To the tune of 'I'm The Leader Of The Gang' by Gary Glitter)

You'll never believe it,
Come on, come on,
You'll never believe it,
Come on, come on,
You'll never believe it,
Come on, come on.

Bjornebye in my gang, my gang, my gang,
Bjornebye in my gang,
Oh yeah!

He's our left-back,
He's our left-back,
It's Stig Inge at the back, oh yeah!

*(This is a variation of the original Bjornebye Song which was first published in the legendary but now defunct fanzine Through The Wind And Rain in the early 1990s after the Norwegian had signed for Liverpool FC. To the same Gary Glitter tune it went... 'Bjornebye's in our team, our team, our team, Bjornebye's in our team, oh ****! He's Norwegian, He's Norwegian...')*

Blame It On Traore

(To the tune of Michael Jackson's 'Blame It On The Boogie')

Don't blame it on Hamann,
Don't blame it on Biscan,
Don't blame it on Finnan,
Blame it on Traore.

He just can't, he just can't,
He just can't control his feet.
He just can't, he just can't,
He just can't control his feet.

(Inspired by Djimi Traore's spectacular own-goal in the 2004/05 FA Cup 3rd round defeat to Burnley)

Blaydon Races

(To the famous Geordie folk song 'Blaydon Races')

Newcastle Brown, it has to be a winner,
Twenty-five pints on a Saturday night and
twelve for Sunday dinner.
We taught the Geordies how to sing,
we taught them how to sup,
But most of all we taught them how...to lift the FA Cup!

(Originally penned by George Ridley – or Geordie Ridley as he is better known – back in 1862, Blaydon Races famously celebrates Geordie life, events and culture, although this Scouse interpretation focuses more on the drinking culture and the Reds' Cup-winning culture with the 3-0 1974 FA Cup final victory against the Magpies inspiring this version)

Bobby Firmino

(To the theme tune from 1980s TV programme
'We Are the Champions')

Bobby Firmino (clap-clap, clap-clap-clap),
Bobby Firmino (clap-clap, clap-clap-clap).

(Used by Kopites for countless players over the years from Terry
McDermott, Ronnie Whelan, Gary Gillespie, Jamie Redknapp, Emile
Heskey and Xabi Alonso right through to Adam Lallana and Divock
Origi, the most recent recipient of the chant in 2017 is Roberto
Firmino, or 'Bobby' as he's known in Scouse circles)

Bolo, Bolo Bolo

(To the tune of 2 Unlimited's 'No Limits')

Bolo,
Bolo Bolo,
Bolo Bolo,
Bolo, Bolo Zenden!

(The same tune was occasionally used to sing Vegard Heggem's name
in the 1990s and Jonjo Shelvey's in the early 2010s, but is now more
famous for being the Kolo/Yaya Toure song that the entire Liverpool
FC squad were filmed singing in a Dubai hotel in May 2015 after Kolo
Toure signed a one-year contract extension with LFC)

Born Under A Liver Bird

(To the tune of 'Wand'rin' Star' sung by Lee Marvin in the film Paint Your Wagon)

Shankly made us famous,

Paisley made us sing,

Rafa gave us Istanbul,

And Kenny was our king.

I was born under a Liver Bird,

I was born under a Liver Bird.

(A song that emerged during Liverpool FC's 2015/16 Europa League campaign, notably when the Reds visited Sion)

Brendan Rodgers' Liverpool

(To the tune of 'Yankee Doodle Dandy')

Brendan! Rodgers!

Brendan! Rodgers!

Brendan Rodgers' Liverpool are on the way to glory,

Built a team like Shankly did, our kids will tell the story.

Brendan! Rodgers!

Brendan! Rodgers!

(He didn't quite lead Liverpool to glory, but this was the song of 2013/14 as Rodgers' Reds took their Premier League title challenge down to the last day of the season)

Bring On Yer Internazionale

Bring on yer Internazionale,
Bring on yer Roma by the score,
Barcelona, Real Madrid
Who the **** you try'na kid,
Cos Liverpool are the team that we adore.

*(Kopites also sing a domestic version of this called
'Bring on yer Manchester United')*

Brucie Grobbelaar
(To the tune of 'Ging Gang Goolie' by Robert Baden-Powell)

Brucie, Brucie Grobbelaar,
Brucie Grobbelaar in our goal.
Brucie, Brucie Grobbelaar
Brucie Grobbelaar in our goal.

*(Never mind the Boys' Pen, there must've been some Boy Scouts on
the Kop in the 1980s as this song uses the middle verse of the gibberish
scouting song!)*

Champions League, We're Having Kebabs

(To the tune of 'Tom Hark' originally by Elias and his Zigzag Jive Flutes, covered by The Piranhas)

Champions League,
We're having kebabs,
Champions League,
We're having kebabs.

(Having previously been taunted by rivals fans with 'Champions League, you're having a laugh' this riposte rang around Taksim Square before and after the 2005 final that Liverpool FC won in Istanbul)

Cheyrou

(To the tune of 'Chim Chim Cher-ee' from Mary Poppins fame)

Chim chiminee,

Chim chiminee,

Chim chim cheroo,

Who needs a Zidane when you've got Cheyrou?

(A tongue-in-cheek chant after Gerard Houllier dubbed Bruno Cheyrou the new Zinedine Zidane on his Anfield arrival in the summer of 2002)

Come On You Mighty Reds

(To the tune of 'Those Were The Days', sung by Mary Hopkins in 1968 and produced by Paul McCartney)

Come on you mighty Reds,

Come on you mighty Reds,

Come on you Reds,

Come on you mighty Reds.

Come on you mighty Reds,

Come on you mighty Reds,

Come on you Reds,

Come on you mighty Reds.

(This repeated verse is most commonly sung but was preceded by a verse that was popular with the travelling Kop in decades gone by)

Corners Of Europe

From the corners of Europe,
To the shores of the Mersey,
Roma and Paris,
Wembley and Turkey.
Fightin' the fight,
For the spirit of Shankly,
One team in our city,
The team that we fight for.

[Bounce]
Liverpool, Liverpool,
Liverpool, Liverpool,
Liverpool, Liverpool,
Liverpool, Liverpool.

(Starting out as a suggested song on an internet forum, it soon took off in the summer of 2008 and got it's first airing in the 4-0 pre-season friendly win over Rangers at Ibrox that August)

Coutinho-o-o!
(To the tune of 'Hot Hot Hot' by Arrow)

Ole ole, ole ole,
Ole ole, ole ole,
Coutinho-o-o, Coutinho-o-o!

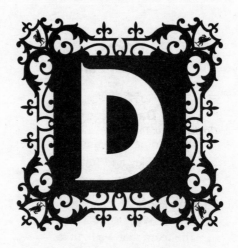

Danny, Danny Ings
(To the tune of 'Daddy Cool' by Boney M)

Danny, Danny Ings,
Danny, Danny Ings.

(First used for Harry Kewell and, more recently, Danny Ward)

Daniel Sturridge

Daniel Sturridge, na na na na na na nah,
Na na na na na na nah,
Na na na na na na-nah.
Daniel Sturridge, na na na na na na nah...

(A song to the same tune was originally sung about Patrik Berger)

David Ngog
(To the tune of The Beatles' 'Hello, Goodbye')

You say Ngog, I say Ngoh,
Ngoh, Ngoh,
I don't know why you say Ngog,
I say Ngoh.

(Penned by Ian Collins in The Liver pub, Waterloo)

Daylight Come And I Wanna Go Home
(To the tune of 'Day-O (The Banana Boat Song)' by Harry Belafonte)

Tri-o, Tri-i-i-o,
Worthington, FA and UEFA Cups.
Not one, not two, but three trophies,
Finished it off with the Champions League.
Tri-o.....

(Rather like 'Biscan In Our Club', this chant takes its melody from a biscuit marketing campaign in the '80s. It refers to the Reds' treble-winning season of 2001, topped off by Champions League qualification)

Didi Hamann
(To the Batman theme tune)

Didi, didi, didi, didi,
Didi, didi, didi, didi,
Hamann!

(A theme tune reintroduced for the German midfielder after it was first used on Nigel Spackman)

Diouf, Diouf, Diouf
(To the tune of 'Agadoo' by Black Lace)

El-Hadji Diouf, Diouf, Diouf,
Won't you score a goal for me,
El-Hadji Diouf, Diouf, Diouf,
Maybe two or maybe three.

With you left,
With your right,
With your head or with your knee.
El-Hadji Diouf, Diouf, Diouf,
Won't you score a goal for me.

Diouf Is On Fire

*(To the tune of 'The Roof is On Fire' by Rock Master Scott &
The Dynamic Three)*

Diouf,

Diouf,

Diouf is on fire.

(First sung during a pre-season friendly in Le Havre in 2002)

Dirk Kuyt Ole Ole

Dirk Kuyt ole ole,

Dirk Kuyt ole ole,

Dirk Kuyt,

Dirk Kuyt,

Dirk Kuyt ole ole!

*(Originally sung by Utrecht fans during Kuyt's time there, this
eventually caught on with Liverpool FC fans and only works if Dirk is
pronounced 'Dirik', as it is in Holland)*

Do, Do, Do (Javier Mascherano)
(To the tune of 'Do The Conga' by Black Lace)

Do, do, do,

Javier Mascherano,

Do, do, do,

Javier Mascherano.

41

Dom Dom Solanke

(To the intro from 'Disturbia' by Rihanna)

Dom Dom di Dom Dom Dom Solanke,
Dom Dom di Dom Dom Dom Solanke.

(Posted on Twitter by Liverpool fans in 2017, Reds striker Solanke gave this tune his seal of approval by replying with laughing and applause emojis!)

Doo Wah Didi, Didi

(To the tune of 'Doo Wah Diddy Diddy' by Manfred Mann)

[Chorus]:
There he was with the ball at his feet,
Singing doo wah Didi, Didi, Hamann Hamann.

Looked up, *(Looked up)*,
Down the line, *(Down the line)*,
Range of passing is sublime.

Woooh Woooh,
I knew I was falling in love,
The kind of midfielder I've been dreaming of.

There he was with the ball at his feet,
Singing doo wah Didi, Didi, Hamann Hamann.

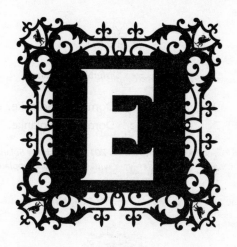

Ee-aye-addio

(Based on primary school favourite 'The Farmer's In His Den')

We've won the Cup,

We've won the Cup,

Ee-aye-addio,

We've won the Cup.

*(Although seen as a generic chant for just about any team that wins
a piece of silverware, this song deserves particular merit thanks to its
Liverpool roots. Along with 'It's A Long Way To Wembley Stadium', this
was the choice chant of the travelling Liverpool FC fans who witnessed
first hand the club claim its first FA Cup in 1965. TV and radio coverage
of the final helped the song gain a wider audience and it soon became
commonplace at each ground although the Kop have always done it best
with chants of 'Ee-aye-addio, we've won the league' regularly heard at
Anfield during the 1960s, 1970s and 1980s on coronation day)*

43

Emre Can

(To the tune of 'The Stars and Stripes Forever' by John Philip Sousa)

Emre Can, Emre Can, Emre Can,
Emre Can, Emre Can, Emre Can,
Emre Can, Emre Can, Emre Can,
Emre Can, Emre Can!

(The same tune was previously used for Ian Rush and 'Robbie' Jones)

Every Other Saturday

Every other Saturday's me half day off,
And it's off to the match I go,
I love to take a stroll along the Anfield Road,
Me and me old pal Joe.
I love to see the lasses with their red scarves on,
I love to hear the Kopites roar,
But I don't have to tell you that best of all,
Is when we see Liverpool sc-o-o-o-ore.

We've won the English League about a thousand times,
UEFA was a simple do,
We played some exhibitions in the FA Cup,
We are the Wembley Wizards too.
But! When we won the European Cup in Rome,
Like we should have done years before,
We gathered down at Anfield,

We Have Dreams And Songs To Sing

Boys a hundred thousand strong,
To give the boys a welcome ho-o-o-me.

Kenny, ohhh Kenny,
I'd walk a million miles for one of your goals oh Kenny,
ohhh Kenny...

(Another famous matchday mantra, although this one has its origins north of the border. Written in the 1960s, the original is the work of Rangers supporters and supposedly signifies an era when they finished work on a Saturday morning, many from the River Clyde shipyards, and headed off to Ibrox for the afternoon fixture. Liverpool FC fans later adapted it and it's still sung at Anfield to this day)

Fernando
(To the tune of Abba's 'Fernando')

There was someone in the box tonight,
He shines so bright, Fernando.
He was scoring goals for you and me,
For LFC, Fernando.
When he pulls on a shirt we don't lose,
That you can bet.
Come on sing along his name again,
He's scored again, Fernando.

(Fernando Morientes/Torres song created by Brian Gubb)

Fields of Anfield Road

Perhaps the most emotive Liverpool FC song of all, Fields Of Anfield Road proceeds to the tune of Irish folk ballad The Fields of Athenry – composed by Pete St. John in 1979. Before being adapted by the Reds in The Oakfield pub, home of the Liverpool Away Supporters Club, in around 1997, it was, and still is, sung in its original form by supporters of Ireland and Celtic, as well as GAA teams and the Ireland, Munster and London Irish rugby union teams. The song was further updated in 2009 to include a third verse commemorating the twentieth anniversary of the Hillsborough Disaster. John Power from Cast and the La's fame co-wrote the final verse and vocal contributions were made by Phil Thompson and Bruce Grobbelaar among others.

Fields Of Anfield Road

Outside the Shankly Gates,
I heard a Kopite calling:
Shankly they have taken you away,
But you left a great eleven,
Before you went to heaven,
Now it's glory round the Fields of Anfield Road.

[Chorus]:
All round the Fields of Anfield Road,
Where once we watched the King Kenny play (and could he play).
Stevie Heighway on the wing,
We had dreams and songs to sing,
Of the glory round the Fields of Anfield Road.

Outside the Paisley Gates,
I heard a Kopite calling:
Paisley they have taken you away,
But you led the great eleven,
Back in Rome in '77,
And the Redmen they're still playing the same way.

All round the Fields of Anfield Road,
Where once we watched the King Kenny play (and could he play).
Stevie Heighway on the wing,
We had dreams and songs to sing,
Of the glory round the Fields of Anfield Road.

Beside the Hillsborough flame,
I heard a Kopite mourning,

Why so many taken on that day?
Justice has never been done,
But their memory will carry on,
There'll be glory round the Fields of Anfield Road.

All round the Fields of Anfield Road,
Where once we watched the King Kenny play (and could he play).
Stevie Heighway on the wing,
We had dreams and songs to sing,
Of the glory round the Fields of Anfield Road.

(The updated Fields Of Anfield Road charity record reached Number 16 in the UK Top 40 chart on April 12, 2009 and Number 14 a week later. The song was also at Number 9 on the UK iTunes chart on April 13, 2009)

Five European Cups
(To the tune of 'Ten Green Bottles')

First European Cup,
Was won in It-a-ly.
Terry Mac, Tommy Smith,
And Neal he made it three.
Moenchengladbach mangled,
By the team of Bob Paisley.
Oh the first European Cup,
We won in It-a-ly!

Second European Cup,
Was won In Wemb-er-ley.
Goodnight Brugge,
All hail King Ken-ny.
What a night in London!

Oh what a mem-or-y!
Oh the second European Cup,
We won in Wemb-er-ley!

Third European Cup,
Was won in Paris, France.
Eighty-second min-ute,
Barney Rubble took his chance.
Real Mad-rid sent packin',
In the ci-ty of romance.
Oh the third European Cup,
We won in Paris, France!

Fourth European Cup,
Was won in It-a-ly.
Brucie's wobbly legs,
And a pen by Ken-ne-dy.
Now we've four,
When before we'd only three.
Oh the fourth European Cup,
We won in It-a-ly!

Fifth European Cup,
Was won in Is-tan-bul,
Three-nil, three-all,
What a mi-ra-cle.
Now it's here forever,
To stay in Liv-er-pool.
Oh the fifth European Cup,
We won in Istanbul.

Five Times
(To the tune of 'Downtown' by Petula Clark)

At three-nil down life was feeling so down,
No-one thought we'd sing – five times.
But the fans kept on singing, never gave up believing,
Let the night sky ring – five times.

'Cos we had Steven Gerrard in the centre of the park,
Alonso alongside him and Smicer lit the spark.
Oh how could we lose?

The players heard our rallying call,
Milan started to crumble, Jerzy saved every ball.
Now it's – five times,
Things are so great now it's – five times,
We're champions of Europe now – five times,
Everyone's singing now – five times.

Forza Liverpool

Forza Liverpool allez allez,
Forza Liverpool allez allez,
Forza Liverpool, Forza Liverpool,
Forza Liverpool allez allez.

*(Where else would you find a chant made entirely of one English, one Italian
and one French word?)*

Fowler's Prayer
(Adapted from 'The Lord's Prayer')

R Fowler,
Thou art is scoring,
Robbie be thy name.
Thy transfer be done,
As a free as it is in January,
Give us this day our favourite Red,
Alonso will give you the passes,
As Carra stops those who pass against us.
Deliver us the title,
And lead us not into relegation,
For eleven is your number,
Forever and ever,
Our man.

(Created following 'God's' return to Anfield in January 2006 and was a reworking of the Fowler's Prayer publilshed in Through The Wind And Rain during his first spell at the club)

Gary Mac

Gary Mac,
Gary Mac,
Gary, Gary Mac,
He's got no hair but we don't care,
Gary, Gary Mac.

Gary Macca
(To the tune of 'Alouette')

[Chorus]
Oohhh! Gary Macca, Gary Gary Macca,
Gary Macca, Gary Gary Mac!

Oh we love yer baldy 'ead, *(oh we love yer baldy 'ead),*
Yer baldy 'ead *(yer baldy 'ead),*
You're Gary Mac *(you're Gary Mac).*

Oohhh! Gary Macca, Gary Gary Macca,
Gary Macca, Gary Gary Mac.

Oh we loved yer derby goal, *(oh we loved yer derby goal!)*
Yer derby goal *(yer derby goal),*
Yer baldy 'ead *(yer baldy 'ead),*
You're Gary Mac *(you're Gary Mac).*

Oohhh! Gary Macca, Gary Gary Macca,
Gary Macca, Gary Gary Mac.

Oh we loved yer Barca pen, *(oh we loved yer Barca pen),*
Yer Barca pen *(yer Barca pen),*
Yer derby goal *(yer derby goal),*
Yer baldy 'ead *(yer baldy 'ead),*
You're Gary Mac *(you're Gary Mac).*

Oohhh! Gary Macca, Gary Gary Macca,
Gary Macca, Gary Gary Mac.

Oh we loved yer Spurs peno,
(Oh we loved yer Spurs peno),
Yer Spurs peno *(yer Spurs peno),*
Yer Barca pen *(yer Barca pen),*
Yer derby goal *(yer derby goal),*
Yer baldy 'ead *(yer baldy 'ead),*
You're Gary Mac *(you're Gary Mac).*

We Have Dreams And Songs To Sing

Oohhh! Gary Macca, Gary Gary Macca,
Gary Macca, Gary Gary Mac.

Oh we loved yer Coventry goal,
(Oh we loved yer Coventry goal),
Yer Coventry goal *(yer Coventry goal),*
Yer Spurs peno *(yer Spurs peno),*
Yer Barca pen *(yer Barca pen),*
Yer derby goal *(yer derby goal),*
Yer baldy 'ead *(yer baldy 'ead),*
You're Gary Mac *(you're Gary Mac).*

Oohhh! Gary Macca, Gary Gary Macca,
Gary Macca, Gary Gary Mac.

Oh we loved yer Bradford goal,
(Oh we loved yer Bradford goal),
Yer Bradford goal *(yer Bradford goal),*
Yer Coventry goal *(yer Coventry goal),*
Yer Spurs peno *(yer Spurs peno),*
Yer Barca pen *(yer Barca pen),*
Yer derby goal *(yer derby goal),*
Yer baldy 'ead *(yer baldy 'ead),*
You're Gary Mac *(you're Gary Mac).*

Oohhh! Gary Macca, Gary Gary Macca,
Gary Macca, Gary Gary Mac.

Oh we loved yer Dortmund pen,
(Oh we loved yer Dortmund pen),
Yer Dortmund pen *(yer Dortmund pen),*
Yer Bradford goal *(yer Bradford goal),*

Yer Coventry goal *(yer Coventry goal)*,
Yer Spurs peno *(yer Spurs peno)*,
Yer Barca pen *(yer Barca pen)*,
Yer derby goal *(yer derby goal)*,
Yer baldy 'ead *(yer baldy 'ead)*,
You're Gary Mac *(you're Gary Mac)*.

Oohhh! Gary Macca, Gary Gary Macca,
Gary Macca, Gary Gary Mac.

Oh we love yer sweet right foot
(Oh we loved yer sweet right foot),
Yer sweet right foot *(yer sweet right foot)*,
Yer Dortmund pen *(yer Dortmund pen)*,
Yer Bradford goal *(yer Bradford goal)*,
Yer Coventry goal *(yer Coventry goal)*,
Yer Spurs peno *(yer Spurs peno)*,
Yer Barca pen *(yer Barca pen)*,
Yer derby goal *(yer derby goal)*,
Yer baldy 'ead *(yer baldy 'ead)*,
You're Gary Mac *(you're Gary Mac)*.

Oohhh! Gary Macca, Gary Gary Macca,
Gary Macca, Gary Gary Mac.

Oh we signed you on a free
(Oh we signed you on a free),
We signed you free *(we signed you free)*,
Yer sweet right foot *(yer sweet right foot)*,
Yer Dortmund pen *(yer Dortmund pen)*,
Yer Bradford goal *(yer Bradford goal)*,
Yer Coventry goal *(yer Coventry goal)*,

We Have Dreams And Songs To Sing

Yer Spurs peno *(yer Spurs peno)*,
Yer Barca pen *(yer Barca pen)*,
Yer derby goal *(yer derby goal)*,
Yer baldy 'ead *(yer baldy 'ead)*,
You're Gary Mac *(you're Gary Mac)*.

Oohhh! Gary Macca, Gary Gary Macca,
Gary Macca, Gary Gary Mac.

Oh we went and won all three
(Oh we went and won all three),
We won all three *(we won all three)*,
We signed you free *(we signed you free)*,
Yer sweet right foot *(yer sweet right foot)*,
Yer Dortmund pen *(yer Dortmund pen)*,
Yer Bradford goal *(yer Bradford goal)*,
Yer Coventry goal *(yer Coventry goal)*,
Yer Spurs peno *(yer Spurs peno)*,
Yer Barca pen *(yer Barca pen)*,
Yer derby goal *(yer derby goal)*,
Yer baldy 'ead *(yer baldy 'ead)*,
You're Gary Mac *(you're Gary Mac)*.

Oohhh! Gary Macca, Gary Gary Macca,
Gary Macca,Gary Gary Mac!

(A cult song for a cult Liverpool FC hero, the Gary McAllister
hoedown is led by one Red who sings a line that everyone else
repeats. Search YouTube for 'Gary Macca on tube' to see just
what an epic song it is)

Gathering Cups In May
(To the tune of children's nursery rhyme 'Here We Go Round The Mulberry Bush')

Here we go gathering Cups in May,
Cups in May, Cups in May,
Here we go gathering Cups in May,
On a cold and frosty morning.

Gerard, Gerard Houllier
(To the tune of 'Go West' by The Village People)

Gerard, Gerard Houllier,
Gerard, Gerard Houllier,
Gerard, Gerard Houllier,
Gerard, Gerard Houllier.

Gini Wijnaldum
(To the tune of 'This Girl' by Kungs vs Cookin' on 3 Burners)

Der, der, der der der der Gini Wijnaldum!
Der, der, der der der der Gini Wijnaldum!

Going Loco With Momo Sissoko

(To the tune of 'Going Loco Down In Acapulco' by the Four Tops)

We'll be going loco with Momo Sissoko,
'Cos he's big and strong,
Yeah we'll be going loco with Momo Sissoko,
This lad just can't do no wrong.

(This tune surfaced around FA Cup final weekend in 2006 when Sissoko was part of the LFC side that beat West Ham in Cardiff)

Good King Wenceslas

(To the Christmas carol 'Good King Wenceslas')

Vegard Heggem scored a goal
on the feast of Stephen,
Vegard Heggem scored a goal
as the fans were leaving,
Liverpool they won three-one
Carragher and Jamie,
Vegard Heggem scored a goal,
all the fans went cra-a-zee.

(Tribute to Vegard Heggem after scoring in the 3-1 Boxing Day win over Middlesbrough in 1998. Jamie Carragher's goal was later credited to Michael Owen!)

Hamann, Hamann
(To the tune of 'I'm The Leader Of The Gang (I Am)' by Gary Glitter)

Hamann, Hamann,
Hamann, Hamann,
Hamann, Hamann, Hamann, DIETMAR!

Happiness
(To the tune of 'Happiness' by Ken Dodd)

Happiness, happiness,
Now its five big-eared ones that we possess,
Oh! I thank Don Rafa that we were blessed,
On the shores of the Efes-drenched Bosphor-ess.

(Another Istanbul celebration song as travelling Reds partied into the early hours on the Turkish strait)

Happy Birthday
(Sung to the traditional tune)

Happy birthday to you,
Happy birthday to you,
Happy birthday dear Kenny,
Happy birthday to you.

(Sung to Liverpool FC manager Kenny Dalglish during the 3-1 win against Manchester United in March 2011, two days after his 60th birthday. Kenny smiled, laughed and gave the Kop a wave back in response)

Harry Kewell
(Sung to the tune of 'Daddy Cool' by Boney M)

Harry, Harry Kewell,
Harry, Harry Kewell...

(A simple but infectious Anfield chant for the Aussie winger)

He Ain't Heavy, He's My Brother
(By the Hillsborough Justice Collective)

The road is long, with many a winding turn,
That leads us to who, who knows where, who knows when?
But I'm strong, strong enough to carry him,
He ain't heavy, he's my brother.

So on we go, his welfare is of my concern,
No burden is he to bare, we'll get there.
For I know he would not encumber me,
He ain't heavy, he's my brother.

If I'm laden, laden at all, I'm laden with sadness,
That everyone's heart, isn't filled with the gladness
of love for one another.

It's a long long road from which there is no return,
While we're on the way to there, why not share?
And the load, it doesn't weigh me down at all,
He ain't heavy, he's my brother.

He's my brother, he's my brother,
He's my brother, he's my brother,
He ain't heavy - he's my brother,
He ain't heavy - he's my brother,
He's my brother...

(A hit for The Hollies in 1969, a 2012 version was recorded by the Justice Collective – featuring artists including Paul McCartney, Robbie Williams, Mel C, Paloma Faith, Gerry Marsden and Holly Johnson – to raise funds for various charities associated with the Hillsborough disaster following the publishing of an independent report into the 1989 tragedy on 'Truth Day' in September of that year. Everton FC had played The Hollies' version prior to their match against Newcastle in tribute to the 96 while two children, one in Liverpool red and the other in Everton blue, held hands on the Goodison Park pitch. This inspired members of The Farm, Pete Wylie and The Clash's Mick Jones, who had previously formed The Justice Tonight Band, to re-record it as a charity single and with the other musicians on board, plus Kenny Dalglish, Alan Hansen and two original members of The Hollies – Bobby Elliott and Tony Hicks – the song was released on December 17 and became the Christmas Number one)

We Have Dreams And Songs To Sing

Henchoz

(To 'Heigh-ho' from Walt Disney's animated classic Snow White)

Henchoz, Henchoz,
Henchoz, Henchoz, Henchoz.
When they attack,
He's always back,
Henchoz, Henchoz, Henchoz, Henchoz.

He's...
...Carragher

He's Scouse,
He's sound,
He'll **** you with a pound,
Carragher, Carragher

...Erik Meijer

He's big,
He's Red,
He's off his ******* head,
Erik Meijer, Erik Meijer.

...Gary Mac

He's bald,
He's old,
He's worth his weight in gold,
Gary Mac, Gary Mac.

...Igor Biscan

He's Red,
He's big,
His name begins with Ig,
Igor Biscan, Igor Biscan.

...Nick Barmby

He's Red,
He's white,
He scored against the *****,
Nick Barmby, Nick Barmby.

...Nigel Clough

He's Red,
He's white,
He's ******* dynamite,
Nigel Clough, Nigel Clough.

...Peter Crouch

He's big,
He's Red,
His feet stick out the bed,
Peter Crouch, Peter Crouch.

...Robbie Keane

He's quick,
He's Red,
He talks like Father Ted,
Robbie Keane, Robbie Keane.

...Sammy Lee

He's fat,
He's round,
He bounces on the ground,
Sammy Lee, Sammy Lee.

...Sander Westerveld

He's big,
He's Dutch,
We like him very much,
Westerveld, Westerveld.

...Vladimir Smicer

He's Czech,
He's great,
He's Paddy Berger's mate,
Vladimir, Vladimir.

He's Alberto Aquilani
(To the tune of US Military song 'She Wore a Yellow Ribbon')

Italy, Italy, he's Alberto Aquilani and he comes from Italy,
Italy, Italy, he's Alberto Aquilani and he comes from Italy.

He's Winning Five-One
(To the tune of 'Sloop John B' by The Beachboys)

He's winning five-one, he's winning five-oneeeee,
Adam Lallana, he's winning five-one!

(During his return to former club Southampton for a League Cup game, Adam Lallana was receiving stick from the home crowd only for the travelling Kop to respond by pointing out the score as the Reds led 5-1. It was possibly the shortest lived chant in LFC history though as seconds later Divock Origi made it 6-1, prompting Liverpool FC supporters to sing 'Adam Lallana, he's winning 6-1')

Here's To You
(To the tune of Simon and Garfunkel's 'Mrs Robinson')

And here's to you, Slovan Liberec,
Liverpool loves you more than you will know *(wo, wo, wo)*
God bless you please Torpedo Moscow.
Liverpool holds a place for those we play,
(Hey, hey, hey, . . . hey, hey, hey)

We'd like to know CSKA or even Feyenoord.
We'd like to help them drink the night away.
Look around and all you'd see were banners made of red.
The famous Kopites singing off their heads.

And here's to you Girondins Bordeaux.
Bottles of red just a pound a throw *(wo wo wo)*.
God bless you, please Zurich Grasshoppers.
Expensive but the girls are worth the pay,
(Hey, hey, hey, . . . hey, hey, hey).
Play it in a country east where no one ever goes.
Play it at Dukla Prague's little ground.
Skonta Riga, Copenhagen, Honved or Liege.
Those teams now never come around.

Allez allez les vertes St Etienne,
Moenchengladbach, Bruges we so miss you *(you hoo hoo)*.
Where are you now Poland's Widzew Lodz.
It's teams like you we really want to play.
(Allez, Allez, Allez, Allez).

Sitting on the sofa on a Friday afternoon,
Watching the Champions League draw come on through.
Barca, Porto, Bayern, Mancs, the same teams once again,
Ev'ry way you look at it, the fans still lose.

Where have you gone, Dynamo Dresden?
A Kopite turns his jaded eyes to you *(you hoo hoo).*
What's that you say, Lennart Johannson,
UEFA have swept the likes of Dresden away?
(Please don't say, please don't say).

Hey Big Didi
(To the tune of 'Hey Big Spender' by Shirley Bassey)

The minute you walked in the joint, Didi,
I could see you were Hamann of distinction,
A real big player.
Good passing, so refined,
You could always play in any midfield of mine.

So let me get right to the point, Didi,
I don't pop my cork for every player I see.
Hey big Didi,
(hey big Didi),
Score another goal for me,
Da, da, da, da, da, da.

Hills Of Anfield

(To the tune of 'Las Vegas (In The Hills Of Donegal)' by the Irish folk rock group Goats Don't Shave)

You may talk about Arsenal,
How they're the best a team can be,
Who's the man in the Man U top,
Is Cisse better than Henry?
But ask them all where's Anfield,
It's not a mystery.

And if I could build a wall around the Merseyside,
The North and South to keep them out,
My God I'll build it tall,
Spain and Portugal, my God we'll buy them all,
We'd have the Premiership in the hills of the Kop,
Yeah, the Premiership in the hills of the Kop.

His First Name Is Lucas

His first name is Lucas, is Lucas, is Lucas,
His second name is Leiva, is Leiva, is Leiva,
And this is why we like him, we like him, we like him,
In fact we ******* love him, we love him, we love him,
Whoaaaaaaaaa-o-a-oh, Whoaaaaaaaa-o-a-oh,
Whoaaaaaaaaa-o-a-oh, Whoaaaaaaaa-o-a-oh.

His Name Is Colin Pascoe
(To the tune of 'Bad Moon Rising' by Creedence Clearwater Revival)

Ohhhhhh, his name is Colin Pascoe,
He puts the cones out for the team,
He wears shorts when it's ******* freezing,
We don't care cos his legs are a dream,
Ohhhhhh...

*(Sung in honour of former Reds assistant manager Colin Pascoe,
this chant was inspired by Argentina's 'Brasil decime que se
siente' anthem to the same tune at the 2014 World Cup and took
off when Liverpool FC travelled to Basel in the Champions League
in October 2014)*

Hou Let The Reds Out?
(To the tune of Baha Men's 'Who Let The Dogs Out?')

Hou let the Reds out?
Hou, Houllier.
Hou let the Reds out?
Hou, Houllier.

*(A widely sung manager chant, partly because of the success of
the Baha Men's hit song in 2000 – it was the UK's fourth biggest
selling single that year – but mainly because the treble campaign
led by Gerard Houllier in 2001 had the Kop in good voice)*

Houllier, Houllier
(To the tune of Boney M's 'Holiday')

Houllier, Houllier,
Gerard Houllier.
He's a man from France,
Who makes us dance,
Gerard Houllier.

Ian Rush

Ian Rush, Ian Rush,
Ian, Ian Rush.
He gets the ball, he scores a goal,
Ian, Ian Rush.

Igor Biscan's Our Hero
(To the nursery rhyme 'This Old Man')

Two-nil down,
Four-two up,
Igor Biscan wrapped it up,
And he didn't know what to do,
When he scored that goal,
Igor Biscan's our hero.

(Sung after his wonder goal at Fulham in October 2004)

In Dublin's Fair City
(To the tune of popular Irish song 'Molly Malone')

In Dublin's fair city,
Where the girls are so pretty,
I first set my eyes on sweet Molly Malone.
As she wheeled her wheel-barrow,
Through the streets broad and narrow,
Crying…

[clap, clap]
[clap, clap, clap]
[clap, clap, clap, clap]
ST. JOHN!

(This song retains all the original lyrics from the opening verse of this unofficial anthem of Dublin City, the one key change being the insertion of the clapping and, of course, the loud proclamation of Anfield legend Ian St John. The 'St John' chant is only bestowed on Liverpool FC's greatest goalscorers by the Kop with 'Dalglish', 'Fowler', 'Owen', 'Torres', 'Suarez' and 'Sturridge' the only others to have their name sung after the famous staccato handclap)

Istanbul
(To the tune of US Military song 'She Wore a Yellow Ribbon')

Istanbul,
Istanbul,
We're the greatest team in Europe
and we're going to Istanbul.

Istanbul 05

(To the tune of 'Horse With No Name' by America)

On the fifth part of the journey...
well we had to get past Milan,
But Maldini scored and Crespo roared
and the **** had hit the fan.
Any other side and they'd call it quits,
but that's not the Liverpool Way,
On stepped Didi and up stepped Stevie
and the Reds began to play.

[Chorus]:
See we went to Istanbul for a football game,
Where destiny called us again.
Three-nil down...The whole world had called it a day,
But they hadn't counted on...The Liverpool Way.
La la la la la la la, la la la, la la,
La la la la la la la, la la la, la la.

After two goals in the Ataturk, me face began to turn Red,
Third goal, and the Milanese, thought they'd put us to bed,
But a story got told of how we just wouldn't fold,
While refusing to believe we were dead.

See we went to Istanbul for a football game,
Where destiny called us again.
Three-nil down...The whole world had called it a day,
But they hadn't counted on...The Liverpool Way.

We Have Dreams And Songs To Sing

La la la la la la la, la la la, la la,
La la la la la la la, la la la, la la.

After 90 minutes then extra time,
it finally ended 3-3,
There'd been praying souls and comeback goals
from Stevie, Vladi and Xabi.
Pulling Jerzy near, Carra said in his ear:
"do the jelly legs and give a cough,"
Then Shevchenko missed and we all got ******,
'cos the party kicked right off.

See we went to Istanbul for a football game,
Where destiny called us again.
Three-nil down...The whole world had called it a day,
But they hadn't counted on...The Liverpool Way.
La la la la la la la, la la la, la la,
La la la la la la la, la la la, la la.

(Written by Nicky Allt for the successful stage production 'The Liverpool History Show')

Istanbul Is Wonderful
(To the tune of 'When The Saints Go Marching In')

Oh Istanbul, *(Oh Istanbul),*
It's wonderful, *(It's wonderful)*
Oh Istanbul is wonderful,
It's full of mosques, kebabs and Scousers,
Oh Istanbul is wonderful.

It's A Long Way To Wembley Stadium
(To the tune 'It's A Long Way To Tipperary')

It's a long way to Wembley stadium, It's a long way to go,
It's a long way to Wembley stadium,
To see the greatest team I know.

So it's goodbye Upper Parly, Farewell Clayton Square,
It's a long, long way to Wembley stadium,
But Liverpool will be there.

It's Only On Loan
(To the tune of 'Sloop John B' by the Beach Boys)

It's only on loan, It's only on loan,
In ancient Greece, We'll bring it back home.

(Created ahead of the 2007 Champions League final in Athens)

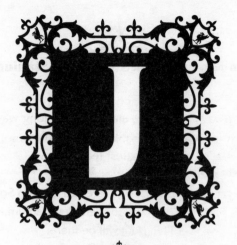

Jari Litmanen
(To the tune of 'Seasons In The Sun' by Terry Jacks)

We have joy,
We have fun,
We have Jari Litmanen.
He's got style,
He's got flair,
Got a mullet,
We don't care.

Jari's All You Need
(To the tune of 'All You Need Is Love' by The Beatles)

Jari Litmanen – da da da da da,
Jari Litmanen – da da da da da,
Jari Litmanen-nen,
Jari's all you need.

Javier Mascherano

(To the tune of The White Stripes' 'Seven Nation Army')

Oh, oh, oh oh-o-oh,
Oh, oh, oh oh-o-oh
Jav-ier Mas-cher-ano, Jav-ier Masc-her-ano.

(Kopites were the first to adapt this White Stripes hit for a player but it has since been copied all over Europe)

Jerzy Dudek In Our Goal

(To the tune of 'Camptown Races')

Jerzy Dudek in our goal, Dudek, Dudek,
Jerzy Dudek in our goal, Poland's number one.
Sander's been and gone, Dudek's number one.
Jerzy Dudek in our goal, Poland's number one.

(Tribute to Liverpool's 2005 Champions League final saviour. The same tune is also sung to the lyrics: "6ft Pole in our goal, Du-dek, Du-dek, 6ft Pole in our goal, do-dah do-dah dey")

Jesus Fernandez Suso

(To the tune of 'Oh, Oh, Oh It's Magic' by Pilot)

Jesus Fernandez Suso,
He's magic, you know.

(Originally sung as 'you'll never get past Sissoko, he's magic, you know' for ex-Reds midfielder Momo, this chant was adapted for Suso)

Jimmy Plaice

Jimmy Plaice,
Jimmy Plaice,
Jimmy Plaice.

(Chanted during Liverpool FC's 1980 FA Cup match at home to Grimsby, a fishing town. It was the climax to a series of spontaneous player puns involving fish. This one refers to Jimmy Case while others included 'Kenny Dog-fish', 'Swordfish Souness', 'Sting-Ray Kennedy' and 'There's only one Phil Eel', while 'You only sing when you're fishing' kicked off the chanting along with 'We are the famous, the famous carpites')

John Arne Riise (I)
(To the tune of 'Hey! Baby' by DJ Otzi)

Johhhhnnnnnn Arne Riise,
Ooooh ahhhh,
I wanna knoo-ooo-oow,
How you scored that goal.

(Testament to the incredible shooting ability of our former left-sided Norwegian. Although believed to have come about from his super strike against Manchester United in November 2001, Riise's goal against Everton at Goodison two months earlier was the inspiration and it was first sung en-masse when he scored against Newcastle at St James' Park in September 2001)

John Arne Riise (II)
(To the tune of 'Waltzing Matilda')

John Arne Riise, John Arne Riise,
Ran down the wing and he scored at the Pit,
And we sang, and we danced,
And we shook the ground that's made of wood,
John Arne Riise scored against the ****!

John Houlding
(To the tune 'The Irish Rover', recorded by The Pogues)

In the year of our Lord, eighteen ninety and two,
John Houlding evicted the Blues,
From their Anfield abode on the Walton Breck Road,
He was tired of seeing them lose.
Years behind in rent all their money was spent,
A bank that held nothing but zeros,
But Houlding instead built a team dressed in red,
Liverpool his Anfield heroes.

(Fans pay homage to Liverpool FC's 1892 founder, although technically when Anfield landlord John Houlding created the team they were dressed in blue and white!)

Johnny Barnes (I)

(To the tune of 'Buffalo Soldier' by Bob Marley)

Oh his father was a soldier,
(Oh his father was a soldier),
He couldn't play the football,
(He couldn't play the football),
His son he played for Watford,
(His son he played for Watford),
But now he play for Liverpool,
(But now he play for Liverpool).
His name is Johnny Barnes,
(His name is Johnny Barnes),
He comes from Jamaica,
(He comes from Jamaica),
And if you read the papers,
(And if you read the papers),
He's going to Italia,
(He's going to Italia),
Oh no no, no no no, no no no, no no no no.

Johnny Barnes (II)

(To the tune of 'The Stars and Stripes Forever' by John Philip Sousa)

Johnny Barnes, Johnny Barnes, Johnny Barnes,
Johnny Barnes, Johnny Barnes, Johnny Baaaarnes,
Johnny Barnes, Johnny Barnes, Johnny Barnes,
Johnny Barnes, Johnny Barnes!

Johnny On The Ball
(To the tune of 'Celtic On The Ball')

[Chorus]:
We love John Barnes,
We love John Barnes,
We love John Barnes,
We love Johnny on the ball.

He's fantastic,
Legs elastic,
He stands proud while all defenders fall.
Shout it loud like,
Shout it all around like,
Shout it in the ground like,
Or anywhere at all, that:

We love John Barnes,
We love John Barnes,
We Love John Barnes,
We love Johnny on the ball.

Jon Flanagan
(To the tune of 'Mahna Mahna' from 'The Muppets Show')

Jon Flanagan do do de do do
Jon Flanagan do do de do
Jon Flanagan do do de do do, de do do, de do do, de do do,
do de, do do do de do!

We Have Dreams And Songs To Sing

Jordan Henderson
(To the tune of 'Mrs Robinson' by Simon and Garfunkel)

Here's to you, Jordan Henderson,
Brendan loves you more than you will know,
Whoa oh oh,
God bless you please, Jordan Henderson,
Kenny said you'll play the Liv'pool Way,
Hey hey hey,
Hey hey hey.

(This is the full version of the Henderson song, which took off when Brendan Rodgers was manager, although it is often sung with just the top three lines repeated and with 'Jürgen' replacing Brendan since October 2015)

Jose Enrique
(To the tune of 'ole, ole, ole')

Jose, Jose, Jose, Enrique, Enrique,
Jose, Jose, Jose, Enrique, Enrique.

Josemi
(To the tune of 'Volare' by Dean Martin)

Josemi, woooaahh,
Josemi, woooaahh,
He came from Malaga,
To play with Carragher.

Jürgen Klopp
(To the tune of 'Live is Life' by Opus)

Jür-gen Klopp, na na nah na nah.
Jür-gen Klopp, na na nah na nah.

(Based on a tune by Austrian band Opus, the Klopp chant took off during Liverpool FC's 6-0 away win at Aston Villa in 2016, although the rhythm isn't quite in keeping with the original song)

Just Can't Get Enough
(To the tune of 'Just Can't Get Enough' by Depeche Mode)

His name is Luis Suarez,
He wears the famous Red,
I just can't get enough,
I just can't get enough.

When he scores a volley,
And when he scores a head,
I just can't get enough,
I just can't get enough.

He scores a goal and the Kop go wild,
And I just can't seem to get enough SUAREZ!

der der der der der der der, der der der der der der der,
der, der, der, der, der, der, der, LUIS SUAREZ.

Justice For The 96
(To the tune of 'Go West' by The Village People)

Justice, for the 96
Justice, for the 96
Justice, for the 96
Justice, for the 96

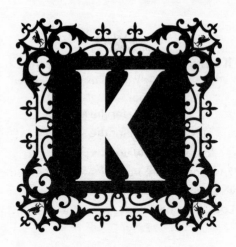

Keane For A Fiesta
(To the tune of 'Fiesta' by the Pogues)

Oh Robbie Keane grew up in Dublin,
With Fowler's poster above his bed,
He's played for Inter, Leeds & Tottenham too,
But he has always been a Red.

He wears the sacred number seven,
And with his pace teams will be scared,
He'll do a cartwheel and run towards the Kop,
As he kisses the Liverbird.

(Robbie Keane wasn't at Liverpool FC long enough for this to ever be sung at a match but it was a creative suggestion for the Irishman!)

Kenny D, The Pride Of Liverpool

(Liverpool…Dalglish…)
(Liverpool…Dalglish…)
It's the time you've got to win,
'cos you know you've got it right.
'77 we lost Kevin, but Kenny joined the side.
Kenny's goal made sure we hold the European Cup,
Look what he's done, we're number one,
Easy! Easy!

[Chorus]:
Wo-ow here we go,
Nothing's gonna stop us now.
We've got the world at our feet,
And with Dalglish in the seat,
We'll do it again somehow (Liverpool!)
Wo-ow here we go,
We Never Walk Alone, it's true.
With Kenny we ought to be,
We're very proud to be,
The pride of Liverpool.

He was capped more times by the Scottish side
than anyone else has been,
When he played in red, Paisley said he's the
best he'd ever seen.
The league, European, and the FA Cup, he's done it all.
With Kenny D it's got to be,
Easy! Easy!

Wo-ow here we go,
Nothing's gonna stop us now.
We've got the world at our feet,
And with Dalglish in the seat,
We'll do it again somehow (Liverpool!)
Wo-ow here we go,
We Never Walk Alone, it's true.
With Kenny we ought to be,
We're very proud to be,
The pride of Liverpool.

Four years on and going strong,
Twice manager of the year,
In the Kop they sing "Kenny's King",
At Anfield they're sincere.
Guaranteed through tragedy You'll Never Walk Alone
And you can see with Kenny D,
It's Easy! Easy! (Go 'ead)

Wo-ow here we go,
Nothing's gonna stop us now.
We've got the world at our feet,
And with Dalglish in the seat,
We'll do it again somehow (Liverpool!)
Wo-ow here we go,
We Never Walk Alone, it's true.
With Kenny we ought to be,
We're very proud to be,
The pride of Liverpool.

(Liverpool, Liverpool, Liverpool, Liverpool)

We Have Dreams And Songs To Sing

(Liverpool FC's 1989 side team up with Peter Howitt for one of club's least recognised recorded singles. The background chanting is provided by The Kop during the Reds' 5-2 League Cup victory over Wigan on September 19, 1989)

Kuyt Fever
(To the tune of 'Night Fever' by the Bee Gees)

Kuyt Fever,

Kuyt Fever,

He knows how to do it.

(The mispronunciation over Dirk Kuyt's surname inspired this attempt around the bars of Anfield)

Kuyt, Kuyt, Let It All Out
(To the tune 'Shout' by Tears For Fears)

Kuyt, Kuyt, let it all out,

He's big and he's Dutch and he puts it about

Dirk Kuyt!

La Rafa
(To the tune of 'La Bamba')

Ra Ra Ra Ra-fa Benitez,
Ra Ra Ra Ra-fa Benitez,
Xabi Alonso, Garcia and Nunez
(and Josemi, and Josemi!)
Ra-fa Benitez, Ra-fa Benitez..
[Repeat]

*(The third line was changed from 'Nunez' to 'Reina' in 2005/06
and then from 'Garcia' to 'Torres' in 2007/08)*

Libpool, Libpool

Libpool, top of the league,
Libpool, Libpool, top of the league.

*(The word Liverpool doesn't fit the chant and although it was
originally shortened to Liv'pool it sounded like Libpool when sung
in unison so Kopites simply started singing that instead!)*

Lisha, Lisha

Lisha, Lisha, Lisha...

*(Believed to be one of the first player chants ever sung at Anfield,
Kopites used to serenade celebrated Northern Irish goalkeeper Elisha
Scott by chanting his nickname as he played in front of them in the
1910s and 1920s, although it was also reported in 1914 that Liverpool
supporters sung "Aye, Aye, Lacey scored the goals" in tribute to
winger Bill Lacey after be netted a last minute winner in an FA Cup
replay at Barnsley's Oakwell to put the Reds en-route to a first FA Cup
final, while there are also suggestions that 'Cham-bers, Cham-bers' was
chanted for striker Harry Chambers in the 1920s)*

L-I-V
(To the tune of 'Jesus Christ Superstar')

L-I-V,
E-R-P,
Double-O L,
Liverpool FC.

Liver Bird Upon My Chest
(To the tune of 'Ballad of the Green Berets')

Here's a song about a football team,
The greatest team you've ever seen,
A team that plays total football,
They've won the league, Europe and all.

[Chorus]
A Liver Bird upon my chest,
We are the men of Shankly's best (of Shankly's best!),
A team that plays the Liverpool way,
And wins the championship in May.

With Kenny Dalglish on the ball,
He was the greatest of them all,
And Ian Rush, four goals or two,
Left Evertonians feeling blue.

A Liver Bird upon my chest,
We are the men of Shankly's best,
A team that plays the Liverpool way,
And wins the championship in May.

Now if you go down Goodison Way,
Hard luck stories you hear each day,
There's not a trophy to be seen,
'Cos Liverpool have swept them clean (with Mr Sheen!).

We Have Dreams And Songs To Sing

A Liver Bird upon my chest,
We are the men of Shankly's best,
A team that plays the Liverpool way,
And wins the championship in May.

Now on the glorious 10th of May,
There's laughing Reds on Wembley Way,
We're full of smiles and joy and glee,
It's Everton one and Liverpool three.

A Liver Bird upon my chest,
We are the men of Shankly's best,
A team that plays the Liverpool way,
And wins the championship in May.

Now on the 20th of May,
We're laughing still down Wembley Way,
Those Evertonians feeling blue,
It's Liverpool three and Everton two.

A Liver Bird upon my chest,
We are the men of Shankly's best,
A team that plays the Liverpool way,
And wins the championship in May.

And as we sang round Goodison Park,
Four Ian Rush goals had made their mark,
Those Evertonians crying still,
It's Liverpool five and Everton nil.

A Liver Bird upon my chest,
We are the men of Shankly's best,

A team that plays the Liverpool way,
And wins the championship in May.

Now we remember them with pride,
Those mighty Reds of Shankly's side,
And Kenny's boys of '88,
There's never been a side so great.

A Liver Bird upon my chest,
We are the men of Shankly's best,
A team that plays the Liverpool way,
And wins the championship in May.

Now back in 1965,
When great Bill Shankly was alive,
We're playing Leeds, the score's one-one,
Up pops the head of Ian St John.

A Liver Bird upon my chest,
We are the men of Shankly's best,
A team that plays the Liverpool way,
And wins the championship in May.

A Liver Bird upon my chest,
We are the men of Shankly's best,
A team that plays the Liverpool way,
And wins the championship in May.

The angels came one sunny day,
They came to take our Bob away,
The greatest sight for you to see,
Three European Cups for Bob Paisley.

We Have Dreams And Songs To Sing

A Liver Bird upon my chest,
We are the men of Shankly's best,
A team that plays the Liverpool way,
And wins the championship in May.

We went to Rome in '84,
We won the treble like never before,
Barney Rubble was the man,
Who won the cup for Joe Fagan.

A Liver Bird upon my chest,
We are the men of Shankly's best,
A team that plays the Liverpool way,
And wins the championship in May.

(New verses to 'Liver Bird have regularly been added - and
there is one regarding the 1989 Hillsborough disaster that
we cannot include in this edition due to ongoing legal
proceedings - although the song lasts for so long it is rarely
sung in its entirety)

Liiiv-er-poool

Liiiv-er-poool, Liiiv-er-poool.
Liiiv-er-poool, Liiiv-er-poool.

(Now the most popular way that Kopites sing 'Liverpool', this version
emerged in the early 2000s and at the time split opinion on whether
it sounded good or not)

Li-ver-pool, Li-ver-pool La La La

(To the tune of 'Solsbury Hill' by Peter Gabriel)

Li-ver-pool, Li-ver-pool la la la,
Li-ver-pool, Li-ver-pool la la la,
Li-ver-pool, Li-ver-pool la la la,
Li-ver-pool, Li-ver-pool la la la.

(This particular Liverpool chant is sung during the instrumental break following the first verse of Peter Gabriel's 1977 classic. It first caught on at one of the BOSS Nights – pre and post-match gigs organised by the lads behind the now-defunct BOSS Magazine – and continues to be sung by local musician Jamie Webster with Twitter footage of a pub full of Reds singing along to it after Liverpool played Burnley in 2017 going viral)

Liv-er-pool (I)

And it's Liv-er-pool,
Liverpool FC,
We're by FAR the greatest team,
The world has ever seen.
And it's Liv-er-pool,
Liverpool FC...

Liv-er-pool (II)

Liv-er-pool, Liv-er-pool, Liv-er-pool

(Generally sung as a frenetic roar and accompanied by arm-pointing when the Reds force a corner after a near miss on goal)

Liverpool [Clap, Clap, Clap]

Li-ver-pool,
[clap, clap, clap]
Li-ver-pool,
[clap, clap, clap]

[Repeat several times]

(Chants don't come simpler than this, nor do they hold as much significance, for this is reckoned to be the song that truly gave birth to the singing Kop. Although countless teams adopt the format, its roots in this country come from Liverpool supporters who, in turn, owe a debt of thanks to a bunch of Brazilians. As the World Cup beamed into the homes of many for the first time in 1962, Brazilian fans, who had much to cheer about, were heard chanting "Bra-zil, cha, cha, cha" during the tournament. It clearly inspired the Anfield faithful for upon resumption of the First Division, Liverpool FC's first game of the season against Blackpool drew a crowd of over 51,000, with over half congregating on the Kop. Everyone was there with their rattles and scarves all intent on making a noise when suddenly someone started to shout Liv-er-pool followed by what they called staccato clapping. The rest is history with the simple ditty now the staple song for most clubs)

Liverpool Are Magic

Liverpool are magic,
Everton are tragic,
La la la la, la la la la.

(A simple chant already in existence before the late great Emlyn Hughes was credited with coining the phrase. He did, however, bring it to prominence when, during the club's 1977 European Cup homecoming, he greeted the crowd by picking up the mic and uttering those very words, encouraging the fans to break out in chorus)

Liverpool, Liverpool, Liverpool
(To the tune of 'The Stars and Stripes Forever' by John Philip Sousa)

Liverpool, Liverpool, Liverpool,
Liverpool, Liverpool, Liverpooool,
Liverpool, Liverpool, Liverpool
Liverpool, Liverpool!

Liverpool Will Marmalise Milan
(To the tune of Irish folk ballad 'Kelly Of Killane')

What's the news, what's the news,
Oh my brave Anfield fans,
As you wait for the game to begin,
Milne and Byrne are both hurt,
But each noble red shirt,
Will pray tonight that Liverpool will win.
Oh my boys they're the pride of the whole Merseyside,

We Have Dreams And Songs To Sing

They're the greatest of heroes to a man,
So fling your favours aloft,
And give three rousing cheers that,
Liverpool will marmalise Milan.

Tell me who is the giant,
With the black curly hair,
He who stands at the head of your band?
Seven feet is his height,
With some inches to spare.
And he looks like a king in command,
Ron Yeats is his name,
The best skipper in the game,
He's the greatest of heroes, what a man!
So fling your favours aloft,
And give three rousing cheers that,
Liverpool will marmalise Milan.

Now in three minutes flat,
At the drop of a hat,
Geoff Strong passed the ball to Callaghan,
Well our wishes all came true,
When young Roger Hunt went through,
And should have heard the roar from the fans.
Well boys they're the pride of the whole Merseyside,
They're the greatest of heroes to a man,
So fling your favours aloft,
And give three rousing cheers that,
Liverpool will marmalise Milan.

(Written ahead of the 1964/65 European Cup semi-final, second leg, which Liverpool FC controversially lost 4-3 on aggregate)

Liverpool (We're Never Gonna Stop)

[Chorus]:
Oh oh oh, oh oh oh,
Liverpool, we're never gonna stop.
Oh oh oh, oh oh oh,
Liverpool, we're never gonna stop.

With you all behind us, we just can't go wrong,
We've got the rhythm, if you've got the song.
So raise your voices, and we'll raise our game,
Liverpool, Liverpool, long may we reign.

Oh oh oh, oh oh oh,
Liverpool, we're never gonna stop.
Oh oh oh, oh oh oh,
Liverpool, we're never gonna stop.

When we play together, we just can't be beat,
Shout 'no surrender', don't mention defeat.
The long road to glory is trodden by few,
There's no turning back, we're winning for you.

Oh oh oh, oh oh oh,
Liverpool, we're never gonna stop.
Oh oh oh, oh oh oh,
Liverpool, we're never gonna stop.

We Have Dreams And Songs To Sing

L – is for League, is it number 14?
I – we're invincible, know what I mean?
V – is for victory, E – ever more,
R – we're the Reds, and we're ready to score.
P – is for Paisley, what more can we say?
Double – O, L – Liverpool, Liverpool, we're on the way.

Oh oh oh, oh oh oh,
Liverpool, we're never gonna stop.
Oh oh oh, oh oh oh,
Liverpool, we're never gonna stop.

Oh oh oh, oh oh oh,
Liverpool, we're never gonna stop.
Oh oh oh, oh oh oh,
Liverpool, we're never gonna stop.

(Official club anthem, released as a double A side in 1983. It reached number 54 in the UK charts. The song was written, performed and produced by former Hollies guitarist/singer Terry Sylvester, an Allerton-raised Red who almost signed for Liverpool FC as a schoolboy when invited for a trial at Melwood by then trainer Bob Paisley. Now living and performing in America, he was inducted into the Rock & Roll Hall Of Fame in 2010 and attended the ceremony in his Liverpool shirt. Terry was in the Leppings Lane during the Hillsborough disaster and is a cousin of former Everton boss Joe Royle. He remains in touch with many former players, including Steve Nicol and Phil Neal)

London Bridge Is Falling Down

London Bridge is falling down,
Falling down, falling down,
London Bridge is falling down,
Poor old Chelsea.
Build it up with Red and White,
Red and White,
Red and White.
Build it up with Red and White,
Poor old Chelsea.

*(Originated during the 1965/66 season when Liverpool FC beat Chelsea 2-1
at Anfield to seal a seventh title. Some make the reference more obvious by
substituting London Bridge for Stamford Bridge)*

Look Out Wembley Here We Come

Look out Wembley here we come,
With our best shooting boots on.
The Cup ties have started,
You think it's a joke,
Each morning at training,
This is what the players are saying,
When at your toe, the ball you get,
Crack it right into the net,
And we'll get to Wembley yet,
Look out Wembley here we come.

We Have Dreams And Songs To Sing

See those twinkling toes of Payne,
Up to his old tricks again,
A flick and a twist,
He's away up the wing.
The half back left standing,
See he's also beat the full-back,
Then across the centre will go,
Directly to Liddell's toe,
Crack! And the rest you know,
Look out Wembley here we come!

(Written for the 1950 FA Cup final between Liverpool FC and Arsenal, a game the Reds lost with both sides unusually wearing their away kits)

Lucas Leiva!
(To the tune of 'Love Is In The Air' by John Paul Young)

Do do do do, do do do do,
Lucas Leiva, oh-oh oh-oh oh-oh,
Lucas Leiva, oh-oh oh-oh oh-oh,
Do do-do do, do do do do, do do do do
Lucas Leiva, oh-oh oh-oh oh-oh
Lucas Leiva, oh-oh oh-oh oh-oh.

Luis Garcia
(To the tune of 'You Are My Sunshine')

Luis Garcia,
He drinks sangria,
He came from Barca,
To bring us joy.
He's five-foot seven,
He's football heaven,
So please don't take our Luis away.
Luis Garcia...

(Dedicated to Liverpool FC's former diminutive Spanish winger. His huge rapport with fans, thanks to the goals that got the Reds to Istanbul in 2005, has earned it cult status and is still sung every time the Reds play Chelsea plus at plenty of other matches too)

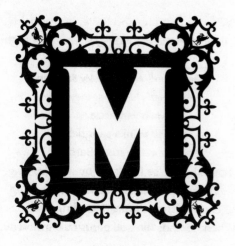

Made For Shooting
(To the tune of 'These Boots Are Made For Walkin'' by Nancy Sinatra)

We'll all sing and raise our glasses up,
When we win the European Cup.
We've got the greatest side in the land,
And we're all known as Shankly's happy band.

[Chorus]:
These boots are made for shooting,
And that's just what they'll do,
And when we get to Hungary,
They'll score a goal or two.

They keep saying we'll do something new,
And rest assured that's what we're gonna do.

When Ian St John and Roger come inside,
They'll give the Honved goalie such a fright.

These boots are made for shooting,
And that's just what they'll do,
And when we get to Hungary,
They'll score a goal or two.

Something else that really makes us sing,
Is Callaghan and Thompson on the wing.
Their centre-forward may find things are cloudy,
When he finds himself beneath big Rowdy.

These boots are made for shooting,
And that's just what they'll do,
And when we get to Hungary,
They'll score a goal or two.

(Penned ahead of the 1965/66 Cup Winners' Cup second round
match against Honved. The game ended goalless but the Reds
progressed courtesy of a 2-0 win at Anfield)

Mane, Mane
(To the tune of 'Sugar, Sugar' by The Archies)

Oh Mane, Mane,
der-der, der-der, der-der!
Oh Mane, Mane,
der-der, der-der, der-der!

Mario Fantastico
(To the tune of 'Rivers of Babylon' by Boney M)

Mario fantastico,
Mario magnifico,
ole ole, ole ole!

(Originally sung as 'Fabio Fantastico' for Fabio Borini, this caught on like wildfire at White Hart Lane when Mario Balotelli made his Liverpool FC debut in August 2015)

Mark Gonzalez
(To the tune of 'Delilah' by Tom Jones)

Mark, Mark, Mark Gonzalez,
Mark, Mark, Mark Gonzalez.
So before immigration break down the door,
You can't take Gonzalez, he isn't illegal no more.

(Written after South African-born, Chilean winger Mark Gonzalez was finally granted a work permit to play for the Reds – one year after agreeing a move to Anfield!)

Markus Babbel
(To the tune of 'Rivers of Babylon' by Boney M)

We've got Markus Babbel on,
Plays at the back,

A big tall German,
Likes to attack.

(Our former German right-back was honoured with his own song during a hugely impressive 2000/01 season. Although later struck down by the debilitating Guillain-Barré syndrome, Babbel admits one of his favourite Anfield memories was hearing the song upon his return. "I'll never forget the reaction of the supporters after my illness, they were absolutely brilliant towards me. There was the Charity Shield game against Arsenal after my illness. I came on for the last ten minutes and the whole stadium stood up to sing my name and applaud me. It was a fantastic reception and it meant so much to me.")

Maxi
(To the theme tune from 'Heartbeat' originally by Buddy Holly)

Dah-da da da da,
Dah-da da da da,
Dah-da da da da,
Dah-da da da da,
Maxi,
Maxi Rodriguez runs down the wing for me.
Dah-da da da da,
Dah-da da da da...

McManaman!
(To the tune of 'Mahna Mahna' from 'The Muppets Show')

McManaman do do de do do,
McManaman do do de do,
McManaman do do de do do, de do do, de do do,
de do do, do de, do do do de do!

Men Of Anfield
(To the tune of Welsh military march song 'Men of Harlech')

Stevie Heighway's always running,
John Toshack is always scoring,
Then you'll hear the Kopites roaring,
Toshack is our king.
Men of Anfield here's our story,
We have gone from great to glory,
We're the greatest team in Europe,
Toshack is our king.

[Alternative version]:

Paddy Berger's always running,
Michael Owen's always scoring,
Then you hear the Kopites roaring,
Fowler is our king.

Men of Anfield here's our story,
We have gone from great to glory,
We're the greatest team in Europe,
Fowler is our king.

Merry Christmas, Everton
(To the tune of 'Merry Christmas Everyone' by Shakin' Stevens)

Mane scoring, all around us,
Kopites singing, having fun,

The Anfield Songbook

It's the season, love and understanding,
Merry Christmas, Everton!

*(Sadio Mane's 94th-minute winner at Goodison Park on his Merseyside
derby debut a week before Christmas 2016 saw this Shakin' Stevens
classic being reworked in a Liverpool pub that night and by Boxing Day
this song was ringing around Anfield as the Reds beat Stoke City)*

Michael Owen
(To the tune of 'Michael Row The Boat Ashore')

Michael Owen scored a goal, hallelujah,
Michael Owen scored a goal, hallelujah.

Mickey Marsh
(To the 'Mickey Mouse Song')

M-I-C,K-E-Y,
M-A-R-S-H,
Mickey Marsh,
Mickey Marsh.

Milan Baros

Milan, Milan, Milan!

*(Milan Baros' chant was sung as 'Meeeeeelan' but it was a bit awkward
singing it at the 2005 Champions League final!)*

Mo Mo Salah
(To the tune of 2 Unlimited's 'No Limits')

Mo Mo,

Mo Mo Mo Mo,

Mo Mo Mo Mo,

Mo Mo Mo Mo Salah!

Mo Oh Salah
(To the tune of 'The Day We Caught The Train' by Ocean Colour Scene)

Mo oh, Salah,

Mo oh, Salah,

Mo oh, Salah,

Mo oh, Salah!,

Mo Sissoko
(To the tune of 'Buffalo Soldier' by Bob Marley)

His daddy was a soldier

(his daddy was a soldier),

He couldn't kick a football

(he couldn't kick a football),

His son he played for Mali

(his son he played for Mali),

Now he plays for Liverpool

(now he plays for Liverpool),

His name is Mo Sissoko
(his name is Mo Sissoko),
He wouldn't wear his goggles
(he wouldn't wear his goggles),
He nearly signed for Everton
(he nearly signed for Everton),
He must have lost his marbles
(he must have lost his marbles),

Mo Mo Mo, Mo Sissoko,
Mo Mo Mo, Mo Sissoko,
Mo Mo Mo, Mo Sissoko,
Mo Mo Mo, Mo Sissoko.

Mor, Mor, Mor
*(To the tune 'More, More, More' by Andrea True Connection/
Rachel Stevens)*

Mor, Mor, Mor,
Morientes, Morientes.
Mor, Mor, Mor,
Morientes, Morientes.

Morientes (500 Miles)
(To the tune of 'Five Hundred Miles' by The Proclaimers)

And I would walk five hundred miles,
And I would walk five hundred more,

Just to be the man who walks a thousand miles
to see Fernando score.

Morientes *(Morientes!)*
Morientes *(Morientes!)*
Da da da da da da da da da da,
Morientes *(Morientes!)*
Morientes *(Morientes!)*
Da da da da da da da da da da.

My Liverpool

[Chorus]:
My Liverpool, the Kop will always rule,
We'll show the world how football's played.
My Liverpool, the Kop will always rule,
Come and join us!
We're gonna take the cup away!

Hear the ground resounding when we walk out on the field,
Ding dong, the Reds are back in town.
All around the hope's abounding
and we know the future's sealed,
For Liverpool the sun is shining down.

My Liverpool, the Kop will always rule,
We'll show the world how football's played.
My Liverpool, the Kop will always rule,

The Anfield Songbook

Come and join us!
We're gonna take the cup away!

Flags are waving brightly and we've got them on the run,
We know a goal is coming soon.
They could try to mark us tightly but
we know the game is won,
The lads of Anfield Road don't need much room.

My Liverpool, the Kop will always rule,
We'll show the world how football's played.
My Liverpool, the Kop will always rule,
Come and join us!
We're gonna take the cup away!

(Recorded by Kop Unlimited with Lenny Rich in the late 1970s)

Nathaniel Clyne
(To the tune of 'Put 'Em High' by StoneBridge)

Ba-bay ba-boh,
Ba-bay ba-boh,
Nathaniel Clyne, Nathaniel Clyne!

Ba-bay ba-boh,
Ba-bay ba-boh,
Nathaniel Clyne, Nathaniel Clyne!

(Like many other Kop tunes, this started on a minibus! The lads from The Anfield Wrap were travelling back to Liverpool following the Reds' 4-2 win at Crystal Palace in 2016 and came up with this Clyne tribute)

Neil Mellor
(To the tune 'Yellow' by Coldplay)

We found a star,
He'll score a goal for you,
He doesn't like Man U,
And he's called Mellor.

The clock it said,
That it was 92,
Oh what a thing to do,
And it was all Mellor.

(Created in honour of Neil Mellor's 25-yard super strike deep into injury-time to give the Reds a 2-1 Premier League win over Arsenal at Anfield in November 2004)

O Come All Ye Faithful

O come all ye faithful,
Joyful and triumphant,
O come ye, O come ye,
To Anfield.

Come and behold them,
They're the Kings of Europe.
O come let us adore them,
O come let us adore them,
O come let us adore them,
Li-i-verpool.

Oh Campione

A cult chant developed for the
2006/07 Champions League
campaign. After seeing a video
of PAOK fans singing it at their
club's AGM, Liverpool FC fans
hoping to go to Greece for the
final were impressed enough
to coin their own words and
emulate the power generated by
the Greek fans. Ten years on and
it is still sung on the Kop.

Oh Campione

Ohhhh Campione,
The one and only,
We're Liverpool,
They say our days are numbered,
We're not famous anymore,
But Scousers rule the country,
Like we've always done before.
Ohhhh Campione...

Oh Kyrgiakos
(To the tune of 'Oh Campione')

Ohhhh Kyrgiakos, the one and only,
He is a loon!
We thought his days were numbered,
Now he plays here every week,
We can't pronounce his surname,
So we call him Nick The Greek.
Ohhhh Kyrgiakos...

(The arrival of Sotirios Kyrgiakos in the summer of 2009 caused a bit of head scratcher with Liverpudlian lyricists, but a few months on, and after a few commanding performances from the club's first ever Greek player, this reworking of Oh Campione emerged)

Oh Liverpool Bill
(To the tune of 'Liverpool Lou' by The Scaffold)

[Chorus]:
Oh Liverpool Bill, you're our Liverpool Bill.
Your name is a legend of courage and skill,
You gave us the league, all the cups and the thrills,
And that's why we love you our Liverpool Bill.

Anfield will always remember with pride,
The Scot who commanded the Liverpool side.
As sharp as a razor – his wit and his voice,
His love of the game made him Liverpool's choice.

Oh Liverpool Bill, you're our Liverpool Bill.
Your name is a legend of courage and skill,
You gave us the league, all the cups and the thrills,
And that's why we love you our Liverpool Bill.

Bill you will never be walking alone,
The Kop will be with you away or at home.
As long as we breathe we'll remember you still,
Oh thank you forever our Liverpool Bill.

Oh Liverpool Bill, you're our Liverpool Bill.
Your name is a legend of courage and skill,
You gave us the league, all the cups and the thrills,
And that's why we love you our Liverpool Bill.

(Kopites profess their love for the legendary Bill Shankly with a unique take on The Scaffold's 1974 No.7 UK hit single 'Liverpool Lou' which was recorded with Paul McCartney and Wings)

Oh Ronny Ronny
(To the Jewish tune 'Hava Nagila')

Ronny, oh Ronny Ronny,

Oh Ronny Ronny, Oh Ronny Rosenthal, Oi!

(The simple but stirring chant for the Israeli who became an instant cult hero at Anfield in 1990. The song was so popular, the format later lent itself to a fellow countryman in the song 'Oh Yossi, Yossi' - see right)

Oh Sami Sami
(To the tune of 'Son Of A Father' by Chicory Tip)

Ohhhh Sami, Sami,

Sami, Sami, Sami, Sami Hyypia...

(Ronny Rosenthal's name was also sung to this tune by some Reds, but it'll always be most associated with the Giant Finn)

Oh Stanley Stanley
(Also to the tune of 'Son Of A Father' by Chicory Tip)

Ohhhh Stanley, Stanley,

Stanley, Stanley, Stanley, Stanley Collymore...

Oh When The Reds Go Marching In
(To the tune 'When The Saints Go Marching In')

Oh when the Reds, *(Oh when the Reds),*
Go marching in, *(Go marching in),*
Oh when the Reds go marching in,
I wanna be in that number,
Oh when the Reds go marching in.

(Another must mantra for matchdays. Based on an old gospel tune revived by the traditional jazz bands of the early '60s, it was an instant terrace classic, and has since been copied by other clubs, including Southampton where many believe it originated. Some believe the song started life as tribute to the great Ian St John)

Oh Yossi Yossi
(To the Jewish tune 'Hava Nagila')

Yossi, oh Yossi Yossi,
Oh Yossi Yossi, oh Yossi Benayoun, Oi!

One Song

One Song, we've only got one Song,
We've only got one Song,
We've only got one Song.

(He may have only played 38 times for the Reds, but Cameroon international Rigobert Song was something of a cult figure on the Kop)

One-Nil Down, Two-One Up
(To the nursery rhyme 'This Old Man')

One-nil down, two-one up,

Michael Owen won the Cup,

When a top class Paddy pass,

Gave the lad the ball,

Poor old Arsenal won **** all.

(Michael Owen is immortalised in Kop chorus after his late double at the Millennium Stadium in 2001 ripped the FA Cup from the Gunners' grasp)

Our Mighty Emlyn
(To the tune of 'Mighty Quinn' by Manfred Mann)

Come all without,

Come all within,

You ain't seen nothing,

Like the Mighty Emlyn.

[Alternative version]:

Come all within,

Come all without,

You ain't seen nothing,

Like our Mighty Dirk Kuyt.

(The rousing rendition honouring our former captain and two-time European Cup winner regularly reverberated around Anfield during the '70s while, more recently, Dirk Kuyt was afforded Crazy Horse's simple four-line stanza)

Over The Hills And Far Away
(To the tune 'Over The Hills And Far Away' as used in the Sharpe series)

The Kings of the Kop come and go,
We stand as judge by what we know,
Our history trophy display,
Those wonderful nights in bonny May.
O'er hills we still reign,
Across Italy, Portugal and Spain,
King Rafa commands and we obey,
O'er the hills and far away.

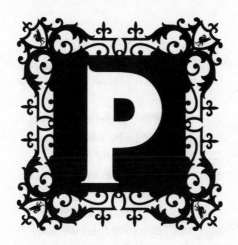

Pass And Move (It's The Liverpool Groove)

Straight out the Boot Room,
To Wembley, our second home,
We come to conquer, no we never walk alone.
We dominate, the cream of the crop,
Drawing all our strength from the roar of the Kop.
It's all for one and one for all,
Pass and move, we're talking total football.
Here we go again, Roy's red machine,
Liverpool the greatest team the world has ever seen.

[Chorus]:
Pass and move, it's the Liverpool groove,
Pass and move, it's the Liverpool groove,
Pass and move, pass and move, pass and move, pass and move,
Pass and move, it's the Liverpool groove.

125

Pass and move, it's the Liverpool groove,
Pass and move, it's the Liverpool groove,
Pass and move, pass and move, pass and move, pass and move,
Pass and move, it's the Liverpool groove.

Go Robbie, go Robbie, go,
Go Robbie, go Robbie, go,
Go Robbie, go Robbie, go,
Go Robbie, go Robbie, go.

Ho shimmy, shimmy, Stevie take it away,
Shaggy's in flight, now it's judgement day.
Digger in the middle, weaving his spell,
Jason McAteer like a bat outta hell.
R-r-red alert, Redknapp in attack,
Jamie's got the look, Jamie's got the knack.
Collymore in overdrive, ain't seen nothing yet,
Stanley on the good foot, gonna bust the net.

Pass and move, it's the Liverpool groove,
Pass and move, it's the Liverpool groove,
Pass and move, pass and move, pass and move, pass and move,
Pass and move, it's the Liverpool groove.

Go Robbie, go Robbie, go,
Go Robbie, go Robbie, go,
Go Robbie, go Robbie, go,
Go Robbie, go Robbie, go.
Go Robbie, go Robbie, go,
Go Robbie, go Robbie, go,
Go Robbie, go Robbie, go,
Go Robbie, go Robbie, go.

We Have Dreams And Songs To Sing

Scousers here, scousers there, Scousers every...
La la la la la la la.

Pass and move, it's the Liverpool groove,
Pass and move, it's the Liverpool groove,
Pass and move, pass and move, pass and move, pass and move,
Pass and move, it's the Liverpool groove.

Rushie's scored more than all the rest,
Respect to the lad with red upon his chest.
You get cut playing with the Razor,
Sharp like Armani, Jamo is the saviour.
Go Jamo, go Jamo, go,
Go Trigger, go Trigger, go,
Go Macca, go Macca, go,
Go Wrighty, go Wrighty, go,
Go Scalesy, go Scalesy, go,
Go Razor, go Razor, go,
Go Babbsy, go Babbsy, go,
Go Digger, go Digger, go,
Go Tommo, go Tommo, go,
Go Jamie, go Jamie, go,
Go Shaggy, go Shaggy, go,
Go Rushie, go Rushie, go,
Go Stanley, go Stanley, go.
Go Robbie, go Robbie, go,
Go Robbie, go Robbie, go,
Go Robbie, go Robbie, go!

Pass and move, it's the Liverpool groove,
Pass and move, it's the Liverpool groove...

(This official 1996 FA Cup anthem reached No.4 in the UK charts)

Patrik Berger
(To the tune of 'Lola' by The Kinks)

He's got long hair and he's strong as an ox,
And he scores great goals from the edge of the box,
His name is Berger,
La la, Patrik Berger.

Pepe Reina!

Pepe Reina, Pepe Reina, ay, ay!
Pepe Reina, Pepe Reina, ay, ay!

Phil Babb
(To the 'Match Of The Day' theme tune)

Phil Babb Babb Babb Babb Babb Babb Babb Babb,
Phil Babb Babb Babb Babb Babb,
Phil Babb, Babb, Babb, Babb, Babb Babb Babb Babb,
Phil Babb Babb Babb Babb Babb,
Phil Babb Babb, Babb, Babb, Babb Babb Babb Babb,
Phil Babb Babb Babb Babb Babb,
Phil Babb Babb Babb Babb Babb Babb Babb Babb Babb, Phil
Babb Babb Babb Babb Babb Babb,
Phil Babb Phil Babb Phil Babb Phil Babb Babb!

Poor Scouser Tommy

One of the earliest and defining Liverpool FC songs that has evolved alongside the club's success. The story is about a young Scouser who's sent off to fight in the war, but is shot down, and with his last breath he utters the verse that begins with 'oh I am a Liverpudlian'. First sung on the Kop during the '60s, it was updated in 1982 when Ian Rush put four past Everton in a 5-0 win at Goodison and was given a verse of his own. There remains some debate about the exact lyrics. For example some fans prefer to use the original 'Libyan' or 'radiant' sun instead of the more popular 'Arabian' sun.

Poor Scouser Tommy

*(To the tune of: 1st part – Red River Valley, 2nd part – The Sash,
3rd part – All You Need Is Love)*

Let me tell you the story of a poor boy,
Who was sent far away from his home,
To fight for his king and his country,
And also the old folks back home.

So they put him in a Highland division,
Sent him off to a far foreign land,
Where the flies swarm around in their thousands,
And there's nothing to see but the sand.

Now the battle it started next morning,
Under the Arabian sun,
I remember that poor Scouser Tommy,
He was shot by an old Nazi gun.

As he lay on the battlefield dying, dying, dying,
With the blood gushing out of his head *(of his head)*,
As he lay on the battlefield dying, dying, dying,
These were the last words he said...

Oh I am a Liverpudlian and I come from Spion Kop,
I like to sing, I like to shout,
I get thrown out quite a lot *(every week)*.
I support a team that's dressed in red,
It's a team that you all know,
A team that we call LIVERPOOL,
To glory we will go.

We Have Dreams And Songs To Sing

We've won the League, we've won the Cup,
And we've been to Europe too,
We played the Toffees for a laugh and we left 'em feeling
blue – five-nil!

One, two,
One, two, three,
One, two, three, four,
Five-nil!

Rush scored one,
Rush scored two,
Rush scored three,
And Rush scored four,
Nah nah nah nah nah nah nah nah.

All You Need Is Rush, nah nah nah nah nah,
All You Need Is Rush, nah nah nah nah nah,
All You Need Is Rush, Rush,
Rush Is All You Need.

Put Your Hands Up For Dirk Kuyt
(To the tune of 'Put Your Hands Up For Detroit' by Fedde le Grand)

Put your hands up, Put your hands up,
Put your hands up for up for Dirk Kuyt!
He loves this city.

(Voted in BBC Sports' top 10 football chants of 2006)

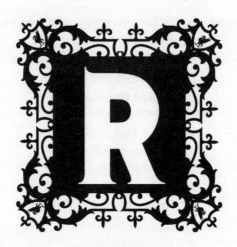

Rafa, Rafael

*(To the tune of the famous old American frontier folk song
and children's favourite 'Skip To My Lou')*

Rafa, Rafael,

Rafa, Rafael,

Rafa, Rafael,

Rafael Benitez.

Rafa's Got His Dirk Kuyt

Rafa's got his Dirk Kuyt,

Rafa's got his Dirk Kuyt,

Nah nah nah nah, Oi!!

Nah nah nah nah, Oi!!

(Pronouncing 'Kuyt' correctly is crucial here!)

Raul the Red

(To the nursery rhyme 'Row, Row, Row Your Boat')

Raul, Raul, Raul the Red,
Bald and Portuguese,
Meireles, Meireles, Meireles, Meireles,
Score a goal for me.

Ray Ray Kennedy

Ray-Ray Ray Ray Kennedy,
Ray-Ray Ray Ray Kennedy!

(This simple chant – which rang around the Kop again in April 2009 when Parkinson's Disease sufferer Ray Kennedy made an emotional appearance on the Anfield pitch – was also sung to Mark-Mark Mark Mark Lawrenson and Mark-Mark Mark Mark Kennedy)

Red And White Kop
(To the tune of The Beatles' 'Yellow Submarine')

On a Saturday afternoon,
We support a team called Liverpool.
And we sing until we drop,
In our Red and White Spion Kop *(Spion Kop!)*.

[Chorus]:
We all live in a red and white Kop,
A red and white Kop, a red and white Kop.
We all live in a red and white Kop,
A red and white Kop, a red and white Kop.

In a town where I was born,
Lived a man who sailed the seas.
And he told me of his pride,
They were a famous football team.
So we trailed to Anfield Road,
Singing songs of victory.
And there we found the holy ground,
Of our hero Bill Shankly.

We all live in a red and white Kop,
A red and white Kop,
A red and white Kop.
We all live in a red and white Kop,
A red and white Kop,
A red and white Kop.

Reds Never Tire
(To the tune of 'Mull of Kintyre' by Paul McCartney and Wings)

Far have I travelled,
And much have I seen,
The years spent in Europe,
Now number twenty.
While all those around us,
All fade and they tire,
You will hear the Kop singing,
The Reds never tire.

[Chorus]:
The Reds never tire,
You'll hear the Kop singing,
You'll play with the fire,
That just keeps us winning,
The Reds never tire.

Now Everton are finished,
And Leeds they are dead,
Benfica and Gladbach,
Their faces are red.
The Cockneys are bottom,
They won't get much higher,
But you'll hear the Kop singing,
The Reds never tire.

The Reds never tire,
You'll hear the Kop singing,

You'll play with the fire,
That just keeps us winning,
The Reds never tire.

Now back in the sixties,
There's Hunt and St John,
With Steve and Rowdy,
But sadly they're gone.
Today we've got Michael,
And Robbie on fire,
And you'll hear the Kop singing,
The Reds never tire.

The Reds never tire,
You'll hear the Kop singing,
You'll play with the fire,
That just keeps us winning,
The Reds never tire.

Ring Of Fire
(To the tune of 'Ring Of Fire' by Johnny Cash)

Der-der-der-der-der-der-der-derrrrrr,
Der-der-der-der-der-der-der-derrrrrr!

[Repeat ad inifinitum]

(Ring Of Fire was played in the Reds' dressing room ahead of the 2005 Champions League final. Steven Gerrard and Jamie Carragher were later seen on television singing the instrumental interlude during the post-match celebrations)

Ring Of Fire

The song synonymous with Istanbul
and Liverpool FC's fifth European Cup.
Although most fans are familiar with the
full lyrics, it's actually the instrumental
interlude that gets sung. Legend says it
began on a coach going to a Birmingham
away game between 2002 and 2004, but
it came to prominence during the 2004/05
Champions League campaign – two years
after Johnny Cash had died. Such was its
roaring success, the club adopted it as their
2006 FA Cup anthem and it was recorded
by the newly-formed Boot Room All-Stars
(Tim Speed and Apollo 440), and featured
the vocals of lifelong Red and Echo And
The Bunnymen frontman Ian McCulloch.

Robbie Fowler
(To the tune of 'That's Amore' by Dean Martin)

When the ball hits the net,
It's a fairly safe bet that it's Fowler,
Robbie Fowler.

And When Liverpool score,
You will hear the Kop roar:
'Oh, it's Fowler, Robbie Fowler.'

Ian Rush, Roger Hunt,
Who's the best man up front?
Oh, its Fowler, Robbie Fowler.

He's the King of the Kop,
He's the best of the lot,
Robbie Fowler.

Robbie Keane
(To the tune of The Beatles' 'Let it Be')

Robbie Keane, Robbie Keane,
Robbie Keane, Robbie Keane,
His name's not ******* Keano,
Robbie Keane.

(This was sung by the Kop in 2008/09 in response to Liverpool FC fans in the Main Stand chanting 'Keano, Keano' – the Man United chant for Roy Keane – after Robbie had scored for the Reds)

138

Rockin' Around With Stevie G
(To the tune of Brenda Lee's 'Rockin Around The Christmas Tree')

Rockin' around with Stevie G,
As he takes us to the top,
Singing a song for LFC,
On the famous Anfield Kop.

Rockin' around with Stevie G,
There's Riera on the wing.
Later you'll hear the fans all cheer,
When Fernando puts one in.

You will get a sentimental feeling when you hear,
Scousers singing: 'Lets be jolly,
Pepe Reina is our goalie.'

Rockin' around with Stevie G,
See the happy Kopites sway.
Everyone dancing merrily,
In the new old-fashioned way.

Roma
(To the tune 'Arrivederci Roma')

We're on our way to Roma,
On the 25th of May.
All the Kopites will be singing,

Vatican Bells they will be ringing,
Liverpool boys they will be drinking,
When we win the European Cup.
We'll be drinking all their vino,
On the 23rd, 24th, 25th, 26th of May.
All the Kopites will be singing,
Vatican Bells they will be ringing,
Liverpool boys they will be drinking,
When we win the European Cup.

Now we went back to Roma,
On the 30th of May.
All the Kopites they were singing,
Vatican bells they were ringing,
Liverpool FC they were a swinging,
When we won the European Cup.

Romeo And Juliet
(Inspired by the prologue to Shakespeare's 'Romeo And Juliet')

[Chorus]:
Two clubs alike in dignity,
In Liverpool where we set our scene,
And Juliet's dad was Everton mad,
While Romeo's followed Bill Shankly's team.

As she was going to Goodison Park,
It being on derby day,
He passed her on his way to the match,
And pretended he'd lost his way.

We Have Dreams And Songs To Sing

"Ello dear Jill can you help me,
I'm sweating cobs 'cos it's ten to three,
If I don't find that Goodison Road,
I'm bound to miss Hunt's opening goal."

Two clubs alike in dignity,
In Liverpool where we set our scene,
And Juliet's dad was Everton mad,
While Romeo's followed Bill Shankly's team.

She flashed her saucy eyes at him,
And, oh, but they were Kendall-blue,
She answered him quite modestly,
"I'd rather be dead than a Red like you,
I'm a Catterick maverick through and through,
And I would die for the lads in Blue,
But I'll guide you to the holy ground,
Lest you miss Alan scoring two."

Two clubs alike in dignity,
In Liverpool where we set our scene,
And Juliet's dad was Everton mad,
While Romeo's followed Bill Shankly's team.

He arched his back against the bar,
To save her from the swaying fans,
They sang 'You'll Never Walk Alone',
And they left Goodison hand in hand.
Well Juliet's dad went raving mad,
And Romeo's nearly went berserk,
But over a black-and-tan that night,

The Anfield Songbook

They agreed mixed marriages never work.
So while the moon was shining bright,
Our star-struck lovers eloped one night,
On the midnight ferry they crossed over,
Now they're both supporting Tranmere Rovers.

Two clubs alike in dignity,
In Liverpool where we set our scene,
And Juliet's dad was Everton mad,
While Romeo's followed Bill Shankly's team.

(The intense rivalry between the blue and red halves of Merseyside
is cast aside in this amusing and artistic interpretation of a famous
playwright's work)

Said Bertie Mee

(To the tune of 'the 'Tenessee Wig Walk' by Bonnie Lou)

Said Bertie Mee to Bill Shankly:
"Have you heard of the North Bank, Highbury?"
Shanks said: "No, I don't think so,
But I've heard of the Anny Road aggro."

*(Originally Sung by Road Enders, it takes the form of a dialogue
between Shanks and former Arsenal boss Bertie Mee although the
word order of the opening line has changed over the years with most
Reds now singing 'Bertie Mee said to Bill Shankly' while Arsenal left
Highbury in 2006)*

Sakho, Sakho!

Sakho, Sakho, Sakho!

(More of a battle cry than a song, the Sakho shout is reminiscent of the old chants of 'Souness, Souness' at Graeme Souness, 'Nealo, Nealo' at Phil Neal and 'Rambo, Rambo' at Jan Molby)

Sami Hyypia
(To 'The Addams Family' theme tune)

In our defensive foursome,
He's massive and he's awesome,
From corners he will score some,
He's Sami Hyypia.

Saturday Night
(To the tune of 'Saturday Night' by Whigfield)

Saturday night and I like the way you move, Divock Origi.
He cuts inside and he slots it past the Blues, Divock Origi.
Na na na na nah, na na na na na nah, Divock Origi.
Na na na na nah, na na na na na nah, Divock Origi.

(Sung in a Liverpool pub after Belgian striker Origi scored the third in the Reds' 3-1 win against Everton in April 2017, it went viral on Twitter and is now part of the Kop's repertoire)

Scouser In Gay Paree

*(To the tune of 'Under The Bridges Of Paris' recorded by
Eartha Kitt and Dean Martin)*

[Chorus]:
How would you like to be,
A Scouser in Gay Paree,
Walking along on the banks of the Seine,
Winning the European Cup once again.

We'll go up the Eiffel Tower,
And stay up there half an hour,
'Cos we won't be too late,
When we celebrate,
We're the Scousers in Gay Paree.

We'll visit the Follies Bergere,
They like to see Scousers there,
The woman are lovely,
With skin like a peach,
But they'll never move it like Kenny Dalglish.

How would you like to be,
A Scouser in Gay Paree,
Walking along on the banks of the Seine,
Winning the European Cup once again.

*(Written by a group of Reds from the Canon Pub in Townsend Lane,
this was one of several marching songs for supporters making their
way to the French capital to witness the European Cup final victory
over Real Madrid in 1981. Fans also repeatedly chanted "Gay Paree"*

145

to the 'Ere we go' mantra, while the famous 'Tell Me Ma' song was given an overhaul for the occasion, as fans sent instructions back home "that we won't be home for tea, we're going to Gay Paree" It was also revived for the 1997 Cup Winners' Cup semi-final against PSG)

Scousers Rule
(To the tune of 'Don't You Forget It' by Perry Como)

Scousers rule, and don't you forget it,
Scousers rule, and don't you forget it,
Scousers rule, and don't you forget it, Chel-sea.

Shankly's Dream

There are many who doubt we existed,
Years ago, years ago,
But they tended to be bitter and he twisted,
Like Big Joe, like Big Joe.
But we'd won five league trophies before Shanks had come,
We had players like Liddell and Scott.
We're the boys from the Kop, Liverpool is our team,
And Houllier's reliving Shankly's dream.

We got blessed by a great man of vision,
Bill Shankly, Bill Shankly.
And he led us out the Second Division,
We thank thee, we thank thee.
Then we won every trophy that football has seen,
'This Is Anfield' was known throughout the land.

We Have Dreams And Songs To Sing

We're the boys from the Kop, Liverpool is our team,
And Houllier's reliving Shankly's dream.
Everybody in the world heard us singing,
From our ground, from our ground.
And they copied us from Mancland to Peking,
Mersey Sound, Mersey Sound.
Then the players would turn up and we'd make them laugh,
Gordon Banks, Franny Lee and Big Jack.
We're the boys from the Kop, Liverpool is our team,
And Houllier's reliving Shankly's dream.

Then Bob Paisley he did even better,
Than Shankly, than Shankly.
Euro Cups in a cardie, trendsetter,
He won three, he won three.
He was shy, he was quiet but by God he was great,
And we loved him just like we loved Shanks.
We're the boys from the Kop, Liverpool is our team,
And Houllier's reliving Shankly's dream.

Then came Heysel and Kenny took over,
From old Joe, from old Joe.
For a while we were rolling in clover,
Watch us go, watch us go.
And he won us the double against Everton,
Wembley sounded like never before.
We're the boys from the Kop, Liverpool is our team,
And Houllier's reliving Shankly's dream.

We were shocked, we were stunned, we were shaken,
When it came, when it came.

All those children of Shanks that were taken,
At a game, just a game.
And we'll never forget them as long as we live,
They are with us now like they were then.
We're the boys from the Kop, Liverpool is our team,
And Houllier's reliving Shankly's dream.

Came a decade that kept us all waiting,
For a team, for a team.
And now Gerard has started creating,
Our new dream, our new dream.
And deep down inside us, we all do believe,
That he'll take us back where we belong.
We're the boys from the Kop, Liverpool is our team,
And Houllier's reliving Shankly's dream.

*(Fans mark the club's journey since the days of Shankly as the
achievements of successive managers are marked in melody in the
hope that Gerard Houllier would carry on the proud tradition of
winning silverware - and he did!)*

Show Them The Way To Go Home
(To the folk tune 'Show Me The Way To Go Home' by Irving King)

Show them the way to go home,
They're tired and they want to go to bed,
'Cos they're only half a football team,
Compared to the boys in Red, Oi!

Side By Side

(To the tune 'Side By Side' recorded by Brenda Lee, Dean Martin and Frankie Laine among others)

Oh we've no longer Shankly and Paisley,

Or a horse that is gangly and crazy,

But we've Thommo and Ged,

Wearing the Red,

Side by Side.

Oh we're leaving the nineties behind us,

In Dortmund is where you will find us,

Wearing the Red,

With Thommo and Ged,

Side by side.

They'll win many trophies,

Just you wait and see,

Just like Shanks, Bob, Joe and Kenny,

They will win more than three.

So we're leaving the nineties behind us,

In Europe is where you will find us,

Just wearing the Red,

With Thommo and Ged

SIDE BY SIDE

(Created for the managerial partnership of Gerard Houllier and Phil Thompson ahead of the Reds' 2001 UEFA Cup final appearance in Dortmund)

Sitting On Top Of The World

[Chorus]:
We're all sitting on top,
Sitting on top of the world.
The team that no-one can stop,
We're sitting on top of the world.

Liverpool, Liverpool,
Proud to call your name.
You touched our heart,
And now we're part, of Liverpool.
Oh how we love to sing:
Liverpool, Liverpool
We'll always follow you.
Through thick and thin,
We know we'll win,
And make your dreams come true.

We're all sitting on top,
Sitting on top of the world.
The team that no-one can stop,
We're sitting on top of the world.

Liverpool, Liverpool,
Always by your side.
With love so strong,
We can't go wrong,

We Have Dreams And Songs To Sing

We're Liverpool.
Oh how we love to sing:

Liverpool, Liverpool,
Winners all the way.
When we walk up,
To lift the cup,
We'll hold it high and say:

We're all sitting on top,
Sitting on top of the world.
The team that no-one can stop,
We're sitting on top of the world.

Ooooh wooooah, oooooh wooooah.
Li-ver-poool, Li-ver-poool.

We're all sitting on top,
Sitting on top of the world.
The team that no-one can stop,
We're sitting on top of the world.

We're all sitting on top,
Sitting on top of the world.
The team that no-one can stop,
We're sitting on top,
We're sitting on top,
We're sitting on top of the world.

(The official club anthem to the 1986 all-Merseyside FA Cup final, reaching number 50 in the UK charts)

Spackman
(To the Batman theme tune)

Ner-ner, ner-ner, ner-ner, ner-ner,

Ner-ner, ner-ner, ner-ner, ner-ner,

Spackman!

(argue amongst yourselves if you think it should be dinner-dinner dinner-dinner Spackman! Instead of ner-ner ner-ner!)

Stayed On The Telly

Stayed on the telly,

You shudda stayed on the telly,

Stayed on the telly.

(Sung to Alan Shearer when he was manager of Newcastle and his team were receiving a thrashing at Anfield in 2008/09)

Ste Gerrard
(To the tune 'Que Sera Sera')

Ste Gerrard, Gerrard,

Can pass the ball 40 yards,

He's big and he's ******* hard,

Ste Gerrard, Gerrard.

Steve Finnan
(To the children's song 'Michael Finnegan')

We've got a right-back called Steve Finnan,
When he plays we're always winnin',
Passes the ball,
Out and in again,
We've got a right-back called Steve Finnan!

Steve Heighway
(To the tune 'My Way' by Frank Sinatra)

Friends, let me tell you of our new sensation,
The man we bought from Skem,
We look to him with great adulation.
As his magic takes it course,
Down either wing along the by-way
And soon the world will know,
His name is Heighway.

Sometimes he's immature,
When on the wing or in the middle,
But with a heart like Hunt's,
The strength and speed of Billy Liddell.
He's got all St. John's class,
And they're the best I've seen in my day,
But more, much more than this,
Has Stevie Heighway.

153

Who is this man, where is he from?
Defenders ask: "Where has he gone?"
He fools them all,
There is no doubt,
This is the man this song's about,
And like the Kop,
You'll hear me shout:
"Give it to Heighway."

My friends the time has come,
When we must find another scorer.
For now that Roger's gone,
I'll tell you friends there's nothing surer.
He played with all his heart,
And gave all he had along the by-way,
And now that he is gone,
We've Stevie Heighway.

At times he didn't score,
But they were times,
Too few to mention.
300 goals or more,
He scored with one intention,
To please the crowd he loved.
And took the praise in such a shy way,
And now that he is gone.
We've Stevie Heighway.

Yes, there were times,
I thought he knew,
When he bit off more than he could chew.
He didn't know the word defeat,

He used his head,
He used his feet.
The record stands, it's in the hands,
Of Stevie Heighway.

Stevie G (I)
(To the tune '99 Red Balloons' by Nena)

Stevie Gerrard for the 'Pool,
Stevie G for the 'Pool,
Stevie Gerrard, Stevie G,
Stevie score a goal for me.

You'll here this song echo around,
From all four corners of the ground.
He hits the net from 40 yards,
Euro glories on the cards.

With Stevie G and Gary Mac,
The glory days are coming back.
And Gerard Houllier's on the line,
As 96 red balloons fly by.
Nananananananana

Stevie G (II)
(To the tune 'Let It Be' by the Beatles)

When we find ourselves in times of trouble,
Stevie G runs past me,

Playing the game with wisdom,
Stevie G.

And in my home, the Spion Kop,
We watch him jog, right in front of me,
Spreading balls with wisdom,
Stevie G.

[Chorus]:
Let it be, let it be,
Let it be, Stevie G,
The local lad turned hero,
Stevie G.

And when the jubilant Kopite people,
All living in The Park agree,
That we all know the answer,
Stevie G.

And although we may all be fooled,
There is still a chance that we will see,
The footballing phenomenon,
Stevie G.

Let it be, let it be,
Let it be, Stevie G.
Spreading balls with wisdom,
Stevie G.

And when the night is cloudy,
There is still a man that we all see,
A young, committed Kopite,
Stevie G.

We Have Dreams And Songs To Sing

Playing to the sound of music,
Stevie G runs past me,
Playing the game with wisdom,
Stevie G.

Let it be, let it be,
Let it be, Stevie G,
For we all know the answer,
His name is Stevie G.

Steven Gerrard Is Our Captain
(To the tune of 'Tin Whistle' from the Robin Hood animated movie)

Steven Gerrard is our captain,
Steven Gerrard is a Red,
Steven Gerrard plays for Liverpool,
A Scouser born and bred.

Deh deh-deh deh deh deh deh-deh,
Deh deh-deh deh deh deh deh,
Deh deh-deh deh deh deh deh-deh-deh,
Deh deh deh deh deh-deh!

(Although the 'Ste Gerrard, Gerrard' chant was more common, it was this song that incessantly rang around Anfield during the closing moments of Stevie G's final home game for Liverpool against Crystal Palace in 2015)

157

Super Dan
(To the children's song 'Skip To My Lou')

Super, super Dan,
Super, super Dan,
Super, super Dan,
Super Danny Murphy.

Sweet Carroll Nine
(To the tune of 'Sweet Caroline' by Neil Diamond)

Sweet Carroll nine, der der der!
You and Suarez are so good (so good, so good, so good!),
Scores all the time, der der der!
Just like Kenny said he would, oh oh oh.

(This tribute to Andy Carroll took off in October 2011 after the big number nine scored on the stroke of half-time in a 2-0 win against West Brom with travelling Kopites singing it throughout the entire 15-minute interval in the concourse at The Hawthorns)

Sweet Sixteen
(To the tune 'You're Sixteen, You're Beautiful' by Ringo Starr)

We went down to the Bridge, we needed a win,
And King Kenny stuck the ball in the net,
It's sixteen, it's beautiful and it's mine.

(Written in honour of player-manager Kenny Dalglish after he scored the goal that won Liverpool FC a 16th English league title at Chelsea in 1986)

Team Of Carraghers
(To the tune 'Yellow Submarine' by The Beatles)

[Chorus]:
We all dream of a team of Carraghers,
A team of Carraghers, a team of Carraghers.
We all dream of a team of Carraghers,
A team of Carraghers, a team of Carraghers.

Number one is Carragher,
Number two is Carragher,
Number three is Carragher,
Number four is Carragher, *CARRAGHER!*

We all dream of a team of Carraghers,
A team of Carraghers, a team of Carraghers.
We all dream of a team of Carraghers,
A team of Carraghers, a team of Carraghers.

Number five is Carragher,
Number six is Carragher,
Number seven is Carragher,
Number eight is Carragher, *CARRAGHER!*

We all dream of a team of Carraghers,
A team of Carraghers, a team of Carraghers.
We all dream of a team of Carraghers,
A team of Carraghers, a team of Carraghers.

Number nine is Carragher,
Number ten is Carragher,
Number eleven is Carragher,
Twenty-three is Carragher, *CARRAGHER!*

We all dream of a team of Carraghers,
A team of Carraghers, a team of Carraghers.
We all dream of a team of Carraghers,
A team of Carraghers, a team of Carraghers.

*(On some occasions the song is sung all the way through from one
to 23 with the last line becoming 'the whole team is Carragher,
CARRAGHER!')*

Team of Carraghers

With his impassioned play epitomising Liverpool Football Club, fans began to dream what a team of Carraghers could achieve. They turned that dream into verse and the tune became the player's signature song, which Carra himself fully endorses: "It was great to have my own song. I don't care who you are, hearing a load of fans singing your name makes you feel good. I'm not sure how a team of Carraghers would do, mind. Talk about catenaccio. We'd be hard to beat but I'm not sure we'd be the most entertaining team."

Teddy Bears' Piechnik
(To the tune 'The Teddy Bears' Picnic')

Der der da der der da der der der,
der der da der der der,
Der der da der der da der der der,
der der da der der der,
Der der da der der da der der dah,
Der der da der der da der der dah,
Der der da da der der da Torben Piechnik!

(Our former Danish defender gets the pay-off line to a children's classic)

Tell Me Ma
(To the tune 'Que Sera Sera' most famously sung by Doris Day)

Tell me Ma, me Ma,
I don't want no tea, no tea,
We're going to Italy,
Tell me Ma, me Ma.

[Alternative version]:

Tell me Ma, me Ma,
That I won't be home for tea,
We're going to Gay Paree,
Tell me Ma, me Ma.

We Have Dreams And Songs To Sing

[Alternative version]:

Tell me Ma, me Ma,
I don't want no tea, no tea,
We're going to Germany,
Tell me Ma, me Ma.

[Alternative version]:

Tell me Ma, me Ma,
To put the champagne on ice,
We're going to Cardiff twice,
Tell me Ma, me Ma.

[Alternative version]:

Tell me Ma, me Ma
I don't want no bacon barms,
I'm going to Cardiff Arms,
Tell me Ma, me Ma.

(Original version first heard in 1977 when Liverpool FC set about winning the European Cup in Rome and then adapted for other significant cup finals including Paris '81, Dortmund 2001, and the back-to-back appearances at the Millennium Stadium in 2001)

Thank You Very Much
(To the tune 'Thank You Very Much' by The Scaffold)

Thank you very much for paying a million,
Thank you very much,
Thank you very, very, very much.

(Sung during Ronnie Whelan's testimonial against Newcastle after Kevin Keegan had paid Liverpool FC £1million for goalkeeper Mike Hooper)

Thanks To The Shanks
(To the hymn 'Amazing Grace')

He was born in bonny Scotland,
And he played the football game,
He came to Liverpool in '59,
To help us win again.
Then with his mighty Red army,
He marched to victory,
He was a legend in his time.
Our hero Bill Shankly.

[Chorus]:
So all say thanks to the Shanks,
He never walked alone,
Let's sing our song for all the world,
From this his Liverpool home.

We Have Dreams And Songs To Sing

No matter were you come from,
No matter who you are,
Remember the year of '59,
When the Reds they found a star.
And now he shines so brightly,
For the boys of Liverpool,
Soon the world was about to find,
This man was nobody's fool.

So all say thanks to the Shanks,
He never walked alone.
Let's sing our song for all the world,
From this his Liverpool home.

Then he asked no favours,
Just hard work, let's get it right,
You can only succeed through dedication,
And his men they all saw the light.
He gave this town his loyalty,
And proved it all by success,
So always remember when we had Bill Shankly,
We all knew we had the best.

So all say thanks to the Shanks,
He never walked alone.
Let's sing our song for all the world,
From this his Liverpool home.

Shankly, Shankly, Shankly, Shankly,
Shankly, Shankly, Shankly...

That Night In Istanbul
(To the tune of 'The Night Chicago Died' by Paper Lace)

In the heat of a Turkish night,
By half-time we were down three-nil,
But the spirit never died,
People talk about it still.

Milan had us on the run,
Others thought that we were done,
But you could hear the Kopites shout,
We may be down but we're not out.

[Chorus]:
That night in Istanbul,
We saw the spirit that is Liverpool,
Brother what a night the people saw,
What a fightback the people saw,
Mercy me.

That night they played with pride,
With heart and soul that cannot be denied.
They gave there all and so much more,
Like all those glory days before,
Yes indeed.

Stevie G got us back in the game,
With a goal that made us scream,

166

Smicer put away a second one,
Now it was time to live the dream.

When Alonso made it three,
With a double strike penalty,
Then the whole place came alive,
And by the end we made it FIVE.

That night they played with pride,
With heart and soul that cannot be denied.
They gave there all and so much more,
Like all those glory days before,
Yes indeed.

That night in Istanbul,
We saw the spirit that is Liverpool,
Brother what a night the people saw,
What a fightback the people saw,
Mercy me.

That night they played with pride,
With heart and soul that cannot be denied.
They gave there all and so much more,
Like all those glory days before,
Yes indeed.

(The never-say-die attitude of Liverpool FC's 2005
Champions League final team is commemorated with this
spirited song although it's never been heard on the Kop)

The Ballad Of Istanbul
(To the tune of 'The Ballad Of John And Yoko' by The Beatles)

Waiting in the lounge at JLA,
Trying to get to Turkey to dance,
The newspaper hack said:
"You gotta go back,"
You know they didn't even give us a chance!

[Chorus]:
Christ, you know it ain't easy,
You know how hard it can be,
The way Liverpool are playing,
She's gonna crucify me.

Some lads got the flight in from Paris,
Some are flying in from Cologne.
Bulgaria's full,
And so's Istanbul,
'Cos the Redmen never walk alone!

Christ, you know it ain't easy,
You know how hard it can be,
The way Liverpool are playing,
She's gonna crucify me.

From Grazer to the Istanbul hostels,
Some lads are staying for a week.
The Major has said,
When the winners are Red,
We're all going to Japan on the cheap!

Christ, you know it ain't easy,
You know how hard it can be,
The way Liverpool are playing,
She's gonna crucify me.

When Carra brings the Cup back to Bootle,
We're all going on the ale for a week.
Rafa said to the hack,
"We're not giving it back,"
'Cos UEFA said we've got it for keeps!

*(Also referred to as 'She's Gonna Crucify Me,' this song
tells the story of Istanbul from the fans' point of view as they
journeyed to the Ataturk)*

The Best Centre Forward's Wearing Red

Oh, the best centre forward's wearing red,
He's wearing red,
Wearing red,
Wearing red, red, red.
Oh, the best centre forward's wearing red,
He's wearing red,
Wearing red,
Wearing red, red, red.
And every time he touches the ball he scores a goal,
Every time he touches the ball he scores a goal,
Every time he touches the ball he scores a goal,
He's Terry Mac,
Terry Mac,
Super Terry Mac.

Oh, the worst centre forward's wearing black,

He's wearing black,

Wearing black,

Wearing black, black, black.

Oh, the worst centre forward's wearing black

He's wearing black,

Wearing black,

Wearing black, black, black.

And every time he opens his mouth he swallows the ball,

Every time he opens his mouth he swallows the ball,

Every time he opens his mouth he swallows the ball,

He's Malcolm Mac,

Malcolm Mac,

Malcolm Mac, Mac, Mac.

*(Reds champion their goalscoring hero Terry McDermott during the
seventies while telling Newcastle fans exactly what they think of their own
Mac – Malcolm MacDonald)*

The Boys Of LFC
(To the tune of 'I've Never Been To Me' by Charlene)

Oh we've been to Nice and we've been to Greece,

And we've done the treble in Rome,

We've been to Moscow and Monte Carlo,

And never walked alone.

Oh we've been Europe's kings and we've seen some things,

That a bluenose will never see,

We are the Spion Kop,

The Boys of LFC.

The Green, Green Grass Of Anfield
(To the tune of 'Green, Green Grass Of Home' by Tom Jones)

The old Kop looks the same,
As I stepped down to watch the game,
There's the green, green grass that Liddell used to play on,
Now there's Hunt, St John and Peter Thompson,
They score a goal when Shankly wants them,
It's good to watch the greatest team at home,
And we'll all be there to see big Rowdy,
And the team that serves us proudly,
When they bring the league championship back home.

*(Stars past and present get worthy mention in this re-working
of Tom Jones' hit which topped the UK charts in 1966)*

The Famous Kopites

We are the famous, the famous Kopites *(clap clap clap clap)*
We are the famous, the famous Kopites *(clap clap clap clap)*

*(An old Spion Kop chant often now sung in response to
'who are ya' barbs from rival fans)*

171

The Liver Bird Of Liverpool FC
(To the folk song 'The Yellow Rose Of Texas')

Have you ever heard of the Liver Bird of Liverpool FC?
Proud on the chest of the team that's best,
The team for you and me.
The team of Billy Liddell, Dalglish and Bill Shankly,
We'll fight, fight, fight, for the red and white of Liverpool FC.

The McAteer
(To 'The Macarena' by Los del Rio)

He flies down the wing and his name's McAteer,
He's from Birkenhead and he talks like a *****,
He cost four mill so he was pretty dear,
Hey McAteer!

The Monster Masch
(To the tune of 'Monster Mash' by Bobby Pickett)

I was working in Melwood late one night,
When my eyes beheld an eerie sight,
For Mascherano from his slab began to rise,
And suddenly to my surprise:

We Have Dreams And Songs To Sing

He did the Masch,
He did the monster Masch,
The monster Masch
It was an Anfield smash,
He did the Masch,
It caught on in a flash,
He did the Masch,
He did the monster Masch.

From my laboratory in Melwood east,
To the dressing room where the Skrtel feasts,
The players all came from their humble abodes,
To get a jolt from the Masch electrodes.

They did the Masch,
They did the monster Masch,
The monster Masch,
It was an Anfield smash,
They did the Masch,
It caught on in a flash,
They did the Masch,
They did the monster Masch.

The players were having fun,
The party had just begun,
The guests included Gerrard,
Carragher and his son.

The scene was rockin', all were digging the sounds,
Skrtel on chains, backed by his baying hounds,
The Kopites were about to arrive,
With their vocal group, 'The Anfield Rap Five.'

The Anfield Songbook

They played the Masch,
They played the monster Masch,
The monster Masch,
It was an Anfield smash,
They played the Masch,
It caught on in a flash,
They played the Masch,
They played the monster mash.

Out from his office, Rafa's voice did ring,
Seems he was troubled by just one thing,
He opened the door and shook his fist,
And said, "Whatever happened to my Mascherano twist?"

It's now the Masch,
It's now the monster Masch,
The monster Masch,
And it's an Anfield smash,
It's now the Masch,
It's caught on in a flash,
It's now the Masch,
It's now the monster Masch.

Now everything's cool, Stevie's part of the band,
And my monster Masch is the hit of the land,
For you, the Kopites, this Masch was meant to,
When you get to my door, tell them Rafa sent you.

Then you can Masch,
Then you can monster Masch,
The monster Masch,
And do my Anfield smash,

Then you can Masch,

You'll catch on in a flash,

Then you can Masch,

Then you can monster Masch.

(An artistic interpretation of Billy Pickett's 1962 US chart topper for El Jefecito that was written during his three-year spell with LFC)

The Pride Of Merseyside (I)
(To the tune of 'Una Paloma Blanca' by Dutch band George Baker Selection)

When the ground is full of Kopites,
And the kick off time is near,
Here's the song we'll be singing,
When the boys in Red appear.

Liverpool – they are pure magic,
And no matter where they play,
When we go all over Europe,
You can hear the people say...

[Chorus]:
Liverpool are the greatest,
The greatest team in the land,
Liverpool have the greatest,
The greatest fans in the land,
We are the pride, of Merseyside.

We'll collect another trophy,
When we go and play in Rome,
And all the Kopites will be singing,
When we're on our way back home.

Liverpool are the greatest,
The greatest team in the land,
Liverpool have the greatest,
The greatest fans in the land,
We are the pride, of Merseyside.

The Pride Of Merseyside (II)

No work, no hope, one chance for fame,
It's our life, not just a game.
For the Reds, grown men have cried,
They're the Pride of Merseyside.

[Chorus]:
With Liver Birds upon their chest,
Liverpool, the world's best.
This great team trusted and tried,
They're the pride of Merseyside.

The angels came, took Shanks away,
And from above, we heard him say:
"Give me the men, whose hearts have bled,
Make them proud to wear the Red."

With Liver Birds upon their chest,
Liverpool, the world's best.
This great team trusted and tried,
They're the pride of Merseyside.

And now our glory will never stop,
We've got King Kenny,
We've got the Kop.
One thing we have, we'll never hide,
We're the pride of Merseyside.

With Liver Birds upon their chest,
Liverpool, the world's best.
This great team trusted and tried,
They're the pride of Merseyside.

(Recorded by Scotch on the Rocks on their 2002 CD
'The Songs of Anfield Road')

The Reds are Coming up the Hill
(To the tune of 'The Kingsman', a military song about the King's Regiment)

The Reds are coming up the hill, boys,
The Reds are coming up the hill, boys,
They all laugh at us,
They all mock us,
They all say our days are numbered,
Born to be a Scouse,
Victorious are we,
And if you wanna win the cup then you'd better hurry up
Cos we're Liverpool FC.

(There's another verse to this chant that some Kopites continue to sing
although the chant often fades out at this point)

The Scarf My Father Wore

*(To the Irish ballad 'The Sash My Father Wore,' more commonly associated
with Kopites for 'Poor Scouser Tommy')*

It was back in nineteen-sixty-five,
On the very first day of May,
Me Dad sang and danced for the lads in Red,
As he walked down Wembley Way.
Ian St. John scored the goal that won,
The Cup we'd never won before,
And as his son I love to wear,
The scarf my father wore.

It is old but it is beautiful,
And its colours they are fine,
It was worn in Paris, Wember-ly,
In Rome and on the Rhine.
My father wore it as a youth,
In the bygone days of yore,
And as his son I love to wear,
The scarf my father wore.

The Torres Bounce

(To the tune of 'When Johnny Comes Marching Home')

His armband proved he was a Red,
Torres, Torres,

'You'll Never Walk Alone' it said,
Torres, Torres.
We bought the lad from sunny Spain,
He gets the ball, he scores again,
Fernando Torres, Liverpool's number nine!

[Bounce]

Na na, na na, na na, na na, na na, na nah,
Na na, na na, na na, na na, na na, na nah,
Na na, na na, na na, na nh, na na, na na, na na, na nah,
Fernando Torres, Liverpool's number nine!

(Known also as the 'Fernando Torres – Liverpool's Number Nine' song,
Kopites used to preceed this with a chant of "We're gonna bounce in a
minute." After Torres controversially left for Chelsea in 2011 it seemed
unlikely this tune - which was also made into an advert by a sportswear
company ahead of Euro 2008 - would ever be heard on the Kop again, but
time proved to be a great healer as when Torres returned to Anfield to play
in an All-Star Charity Match in 2015 it once again rang out)

There's A Man From France
(To the French national anthem 'La Marseillaise')

There's a man from France that makes us dance,
His name is Gerard Houllier.
Ger-ard Hou-llier!
Ger-ard Hou-llier!
Gerard, Gerard, Gerard Houliier,
Gerard Houllier!

There's Only One Freddie Boswell

One Freddie Boswell,
There's only one Freddie Boswell,
One Freddie Boswell.

(Sung to chairman David Moores when he opened the Centenary Stand in 1992. The same song has also been used for numerous players with a couple of more recent examples being Andy Carroll and Martin Skrtel)

These Reds Are Your Reds
(To the tune of Woody Guthrie's 'This Land Is Your Land')

[Chorus]:
These Reds are your Reds,
These Reds are my Reds.
From Bill Shankly, to Rafa Benitez;
From Robbie Fowler to Fernando Torres,
These Reds they play for you and me.

As I was sitting here in L4,
All around me I heard the Kop roar,
And below me I saw the Reds score,
These Reds they play for you and me.

In Rome they conquered and I followed their footsteps,
The crown they reclaimed in the Istanbul desert,

We Have Dreams And Songs To Sing

And all around me voices were sounding,
These Reds they play for you and me.
These Reds are your Reds,
These Reds are my Reds.
From Bill Shankly, to Rafa Benitez;
From Robbie Fowler to Fernando Torres,
These Reds they play for you and me.

When the sun comes shining, the boys are strolling,
And the grass is waving and the net keeps rolling,
As the cup is lifted and voices chanting,
These Reds they play for you and me.

The Reds will not yield as they see a proud sign,
And on the sign it says: "This Is Anfield,"
And on the other side the Kop is singing,
These Reds they play for you and me.

These Reds are your Reds,
These Reds are my Reds.
From Bill Shankly, to Rafa Benitez;
From Robbie Fowler to Fernando Torres,
These Reds they play for you and me.

In the seats around me I see my people,
And on the pitch I see my people,
As they keep winning, we stand singing,
These Reds they play for you and me.

Nobody living can ever stop us,
As we keep walking the glory highway,
Nobody living can ever make us turn back,
These Reds they play for you and me.

These Reds are your Reds,
These Reds are my Reds.
From Bill Shankly, to Rafa Benitez;
From Robbie Fowler to Fernando Torres,
These Reds they play for you and me.

This Could Be
(To the tune of 'Rotterdam' by the Beautiful South)

This could be Parc de Princes or Wem-ber-ley,
Liverpool or Rome.
And when we go to Rotterdam,
We'll bring the cup back home,
Bring the cup back home.

(Sung on European nights as the Reds sought to land the now
defunct European Cup Winners' Cup during the 1996/97 season.
It was the trip to Parc de Princes which proved their undoing
however. Unable to overturn a 3-0 semi-final first leg deficit to
Paris St Germain, the Reds were denied a showpiece final against
eventual winners Barcelona in Rotterdam)

Three Little Birds
(To the tune of 'Three Little Birds' by Bob Marley

Singing don't worry 'bout a thing,
Cos every little thing gonna be alright.
Singing don't worry 'bout a thing,
Cos every little thing gonna be alright.

(The song of Liverpool's 2015/16 Europa League campaign under Jürgen Klopp, this really caught on during the away trip to Borussia Dortmund with travelling Kopites belting it out during the half-time interval at the Westfalenstadion. Ahead of the final in Basel, thousands of Reds were recorded singing it in Der Barfusserplatz and it has remained popular on the Kop ever since)

Times They Are A-Changin'
(To the tune of 'The Times They Are a-Changin' by Bob Dylan)

I've supported this team, through man and boy,
I've treasured their glories, like a favourite toy.
Yet in times recent passed, our mantle had gone,
To the theatre of a thousand prawn sarnies!
But their fun in the sun, has it now come and gone?
For the times they are-a-changin'

I've delighted when I sighted Dalglish pass to Rush,
I've marvelled at McMahon give the midfield the push.
The Grob at the back whilst Digger attacked,
The Championship never in doubt!

Those days long ago, are they coming back home?
For the times they are-a-changin'

Well off went King Kenny we bade him farewell,
Along came old Souness, he gave us sheer hell!
Dear Roy you could feel his team had no steel,
But a Frenchman lies waiting to heal it!
With style, respect, and time to reflect,
For the times they are-a-changin'

With a five-year plan and a warm gentle hand,
Our 'Kopite from France' has made us all dance.
Five trophies in six months you just can't believe,
Get the Brasso, the duster, and roll up your sleeves!
Monsieur Houllier, I bow, you're the toast of the town!
For the times they are-a-changin'

Then one of our heroes he walks right away,
Young Robbie Fowler a very sad day.
A very strange sight to see him in white,
But bring on the stars of Senegal!
With power and pace, and smiles on their faces!
For the times they are-a-changin'

We've a squad to be proud in this famous old ground,
Our manager and coaches the best all around.
Dignity, belief, commitment and class,
The Holy Grail – is it within our grasp?
Let the Reds out, let's all sing and shout,
For the times they are-a-changin'

I said let the Reds out,

Let's all sing and shout,

For the times they are-a-changin'

(Created in 2002 to mark the club's changing fortunes under Gerard Houllier)

Titi Camara

(To the children's song 'Skip To My Lou')

Ti-ti, Ti-ti Ti,

Ti-ti, Ti-ti Ti,

Ti-ti, Ti-ti Ti,

Ti-ti Ti Camara

(The Guinean striker is recalled fondly in this simple chant, the format of which has been made famous by 'Super Danny Murphy' among others)

Tommy Mascherano

(To the tune of 'Don't Cry For Me Argentina' by Madonna)

Mascherano from Argentina,

The truth is he is a Scouser,

He hates United,

He hates the Blue*****,

His real name's Tommy,

Mascherano...

(A modern day Liverpool FC hard man was given the forename of the original Anfield Iron, Tommy Smith, in this Evita adaptation)

Too Good To Be True

(To the tune of 'Can't Take My Eyes Off You' by Frankie Valli)

You're just too good to be Blue,
Can't take the ball off of you,
You've got a heavenly touch,
You pass like Souness to Rush,
And when we're all ****** in the bars,
We thank the Lord that you're ours,
You're just to good to be true,
Can't take the ball off of you.

Oh Steven, Steven, Steven Gerrard,
Oh Steven, Steven, Steven Gerrard,
Oh Steven, Steven, Steven Gerrard,
Oh Steven Steven Geeeer-raaaard.
Oh Steven Gerrard,
Because he hates Man U,
Oh Steven Gerrard,
He hates the Blue***** too,
Oh Steven Gerrard,
You're a Red through and through.

[Repeat last verse]

Twelve Days Of Christmas
(To the festive tune of 'Twelve Days Of Christmas')

On the 12th day of Christmas my true love gave to me,

12 David Hodgson,

11 Graeme Souness,

10 Craig Johnston,

9 Ian Rush,

8 Sammy Lee,

7 Kenny Dalglish,

6 Alan Hansen,

5 Ronnie Whelan,

4 Mark Lawrenson,

3 Barney Rubble,

2 Philip Neal,

And Brucie in our goal.

(The abridged version of the alternative Christmas classic. Fans with more wind in their lungs can go through the whole repertoire of the song, repeating each line, much like the traditional offering as they build up to the twelfth day. This was the team - bar Ronnie Whelan - that played in a 2-1 win at West Bromwich Albion on Boxing Day 1983)

Underneath The Floodlights
(To the tune of German love song 'Lili Marlene')

Underneath the floodlights, down in Dusseldorf,
All the kop were singing, bevvied up of course.
We've been to Lisbon and to Rome,
And our team 'never walk alone,'
We're going off to Europe to bring the cup back home.

All the way from Anfield to the gates of Rome,
All the way from Anfield to bring the trophy home.
Nothing can stop us come what may,
We'll have our say, this is our day,
Liverpool's red army, is marching on its way.

(Based on the song 'Lili Marlene', this Kop song first emerged in the late Seventies. The original song was based on a German poem from 1915 and soon became a favourite of both German and American troops during the Second World War)

Vladi Smicer
(To 'The Flintstones' theme tune)

Smicer, Vladi Smicer,
He's the greatest player in history.
From the Czech Republic,
He's about to score a goal for me.

We Are Liverpool (Tra La La La La)
(To the tune of Boney M's 'Brown Girl In The Ring')

We are Liverpool, tra la la la la,
We are Liverpool, tra la la la la la,
We are Liverpool, tra la la la la,
We're the best football team in the land – yes we are!

Poetry in motion, tra la la la la,
Poetry in motion, tra la la la la la,
Poetry in motion, tra la la la la,
We're the best football team in the land – yes we are!

*(Originally a 'B side' on the 1978 single 'Hail To The Kop', this song was
revived by Kopites in 2013/14 as Brendan Rodgers' side challenged for the
Premier League title while playing some fantastic football and has continued
to be sung during the Jürgen Klopp era)*

We Are The Pride Of All Europe

We are the pride of all Europe,
The cocks of the north,
We hate United and Cockneys of course,
We only drink whiskey,
And bottles of brown,
The Liverpool boys are in town.
Na na na na na na na na...

We Can Do It

Yeah, we can do it,
Yeah we can do it,
Yeah, yeah, yeah.

[Chorus]:
We can really move,
(Yeah, we can do it),
We can really move,
(Yeah, we can do it),
We can really move,
(Yeah, we can do it),
We can really move, we can do it, we can do it.

We can really move,
(Yeah, we can do it),

We can really move,
(Yeah, we can do it),
We can really move,
(Yeah, we can do it),
We can really move, we can do it, we can do it.

You remember '65?
We really had the place alive,
We had it all on our side,
We took 'em all for a ride.

Now we're back and we're here to stay,
We're really gonna take it all away,
We come along and this is it,
We can really do it, now we're back again.

We can do it, we can do it, we can, really move
We're ahead right now and we just can't lose,
We really are good news.
We can do it, we can do it, we can, really move.

We can really move,
(Yeah, we can do it),
We can really move,
(Yeah, we can do it),
We can really move,
(Yeah, we can do it),
We can really move, we can do it, we can do it.

We can really move,
(Yeah, we can do it),
We can really move,

We Have Dreams And Songs To Sing

(Yeah, we can do it),
We can really move,
(Yeah, we can do it),
We can really move, we can do it, we can do it.

We really moving, we're havin' fun.
We got the others on the run,
It looks good and we feel the same,
What we done before we can do again.

We got it goin', we got it made,
We leave the others in the shade,
This time we're gonna show them how,
We can do it, we can do it, we can, do it now.

We can do it, we can do it, we can, really move
We're ahead right now and we just can't lose,
We really are good news.
We can do it, we can do it, we can, really move.

We can really move,
(Yeah, we can do it),
We can really move,
(Yeah, we can do it),
We can really move,
(Yeah, we can do it),
We can really move, we can do it, we can do it.

We can do it, we can do it, we can, really move
We're ahead right now and we just can't lose,
We really are good news.
We can do it, we can do it, we can, really move.

We can do it, we can do it, we can, really move
We're ahead right now and we just can't lose,
We got style and we can prove,
We can do it, we can do it, we can, really move.

*(The official club anthem to the 1977 FA Cup final with Manchester United,
reaching number 15 in the UK charts)*

We Love You Liverpool, We Do

[Chorus]:
We love you Liverpool, we do,
We love you Liverpool, we do,
We love you Liverpool, we do,
Oh Liverpool we love you.

Shankly is our hero, he showed us how to play,
The mighty Reds of Europe are out to win today.
He made a team of champions, with every man a king,
And every game we love to win, and this is what we sing:

We love you Liverpool, we do,
We love you Liverpool, we do,
We love you Liverpool, we do,
Oh Liverpool we love you.

Clemence is our goalie, the best there is around,
And Keegan is the greatest that Shankly ever found.
Heighway is our favourite, a wizard of the game,
And here's the mighty Toshack to do it once again.

We Have Dreams And Songs To Sing

We love you Liverpool, we do,
We love you Liverpool, we do,
We love you Liverpool, we do,
Oh Liverpool we love you.

We've won the league, we've won the cup,
We're masters of the game.
And just to prove how good we are,
We'll do it all again.
We've got another team to beat and so we've got to try,
'Cos we're the best in all the land,
And that's the reason why:

We love you Liverpool, we do,
We love you Liverpool, we do,
We love you Liverpool, we do,
Oh Liverpool we love you.

(Another regularly heard chant at Anfield, although only the chorus usually gets an airing. It's also fitting that it originates from a song about The Beatles entitled: 'We Love The Beatles, We Do' which was a 1964 hit for an American group)

We Shall Not Be Moved

We shall not, we shall not be moved,
We shall not, we shall not be moved,
Just like the team, that's gonna win the European Cup
(AGAIN!)
We shall not be moved.

(An old union protest song of American origins that was reshaped by fans of Shankly's Championship-winning side to a song of triumphant defiance with the original third line being 'just like the team that's gonna win the Football League (again)'. It became one of the regular chants as the Kop sparked into tune during the '60s and has been copied by more or less every set of supporters)

We Three Kings
(To the tune of Christmas carol 'We Three Kings Of Orient Are')

We three cups of Liverpool are:
Worthington, FA and UEFA.
Thanks to Hyypia,
We will beat yer,
Travelling from afar.

We Won It Five Times
(To the tune of 'Sloop John B' by The Beach Boys)

We won it at Wem-ber-lee,
We won it in Gay Paree,
In '77 and '84 it was Rome.

[Chorus]:
We won it five times,
We won it five times,
In Istanbul, we won it five times.

We Have Dreams And Songs To Sing

When Emlyn lifted it high,
He lit up the Roman sky,
Thommo in Paris and Souness did it as well.

We won it five times,
We won it five times,
In Istanbul, we won it five times.

At Wembley we won it at home,
Took 26,000 to Rome,
20,000 to Paris when we won it again.

We won it five times,
We won it five times,
In Istanbul, we won it five times.

Stevie G's eyes lit up,
As he lifted the European Cup,
21 years and now it's coming back home.
We won it five times,
We won it five times,
In Istanbul, we won it five times.

(Written before the 2005 Champions League final and then added
to, the original chorus was "We've won it four times, we've won
it four times, in Istanbul, we'll win it five times," but this had to be
swiftly updated after the events of 25 May 2005! Still sung now,
it's generally the chorus that gets aired on matchdays rather than
the full version)

We'll Be Coming
(To the Tartan Army tune 'We'll Be Coming')

We'll be coming,

We'll be coming,

We'll be coming down the road,

When you hear the noise of the Billy Shankly boys,

We'll be coming down the road.

Wem-ber-lee, Wem-ber-lee
(To the tune of US Military song 'She Wore a Yellow Ribbon')

Wem-ber-lee, Wem-ber-lee,

We're the greatest team in Europe and we're going to
Wem-ber-lee.

(A long standing Kop chant when the Reds are on a cup run, it was popular in 1977/78 when Bob Paisley's side retained the European Cup at Wembley by beating Bruges in the final but the song itself was first copyrighted in 1917 and made famous by the 1949 movie of the same name)

Wembley's Our Second Home
(To the tune of 'In My Liverpool Home' by Pete McGovern)

Wembley's our second home,

Wembley's our second home,

We're going to Wembley to cheer on our team,
To fight for the best team that we've ever seen,
And watch Emlyn Hughes get the cup off the Queen,
Wembley's our second home.
From our Liverpool home,
The Reds will go marching to Rome.
We'll give Moenchengladbach a night to forget,
As goal after goal flies into their net.
Borussia won't beat us 'cos we are the best,
The Reds will go marching to Rome.

*(Away fans have their own version of this song they troll Liverpool FC
fans with but this version was penned in 1977 as Bob Paisley's men were
chasing a treble of league, European Cup and FA Cup)*

We're A Happy Band

We sing our songs with joy and pride,
Every time we watch our side,
In all the league we are top,
We're members of the mighty Kop (mighty Kop).

*Liverpool supporters we're a happy band (ee-aye-addio),
That's because we're following the best team in the land.*

We're leaving in the morning light,
Flying on a chartered plane,
By noon we'll be in Budapest,
By nine we'll know which team is best (team is best).

Hungarians may laugh and grin,

But wait till Roger bangs one in,

And St John will make them frown,

We'll bring the iron curtain down (curtain down).

Their goulash may be up to scratch,

But that won't help them win the match,

When the winning goal brings down the house,

They'll all resort to eating Scouse (eating Scouse).

*(Travelling Kopites prepare for the trip to the Hungarian capital to
face Honved in the third round of the Cup Winners' Cup in 1966 –
a game which finished goalless, although the Reds progressed to
the semi-finals with a 2-0 second leg victory at Anfield)*

We're Gonna Win The League
(To the tune 'For He's A Jolly Good Fellow')

We're gonna win the league,

We're gonna win the league,

And now you're gonna believe us,

And now you're gonna believe us,

And now you're gonna believe us,

We're gonna win the league.

*(Now a traditional football chant, it was most common on the
Anfield terraces during the success-strewn days of the '60s to '80s
when Kopites would sing it from September through to May)*

We're On The March
(To the tune of 'Tramp Tramp Tramp the Boys are Marching'
by George F Root)

We're on the march with Jürgen's army,
We're all going to Wem-ber-lee.
And we'll really shake 'em up when we win the FA Cup,
Cos Liverpool's the greatest football team.

(Another long-standing cup-run song that has featured most Liverpool FC
managers down the years but never Gerard Houllier as all the Reds' cup-
runs under his management came when Wembley was being rebuilt and
the finals were held in Cardiff. The song itself dates back to 1846 and the
American Civil War, but has been used by supporters of various clubs and
was famously recorded as 'Ally's Tartan Army' for Scotland's 1978 World
Cup song)

We're The Best Behaved Supporters In The Land
(To the tune of 'She'll Be Coming 'Round the Mountain')

We're the best behaved supporters in the land
(when we win!),
We're the best behaved supporters in the land
(when we win!),
We're the best behaved supporters,
best behaved supporters,
The best behaved supporters in the land
(when we win!)
But we're a right shower of ******* when we lose
(but we don't!),

We're a right shower of ******* when we lose
(but we don't!),
We're a right shower of *******, a right shower of ********,
A right shower of ******** when we lose
(but we don't!)

We're The Pride Of Merseyside
(To the tune of 'O Guide Me O Thou Great Redeemer')

We're the pride, we're the pride,
We're the pride of Merseyside.
We're the pride of Merseyside!

(Sung to the 'Bread of Heaven' lines in the hymn, this chant was notably directed towards Evertonians in 1986 when the Reds pipped the Blues to a first league and cup double although before the all-Merseyside FA Cup final at Wembley both sets of fans sang 'Are you watching Manchester?' to the same tune. Kopites subsequently adapted it to 'Where were you in Istanbul?' to greet Chelsea fans after Liverpool beat them in the 2005 Champions League semi-final)

We've Got A Big Pole In Our Goal
(To the tune of 'The Whole World In His Hands')

We've got a big Pole in our goal,
We've got a big Pole in our goal,
We've got a big Pole in our goal,
We've got a big Pole in our goal.

(A song for 2005 Champions League final hero Jerzy Dudek, first heard shortly after his 2001 arrival from Feyenoord)

We've Got That Ronnie Whelan
(To the tune of 'You've Lost That Loving Feeling' by The Righteous Brothers)

We've got that Ronniieeeee Whelan,
Wooooah that Ronnie Whelan.

What A Waste Of Money

What a waste of money!

*(Sung to in ironic fashion to inspirational free transfer signing Gary
McAllister after his last game for Liverpool against Ipswich Town in 2002.
Gary Mac saw the funny side and applauded the Kop with a big smile on his
face when it rang out during the traditional lap of appreciation)*

When Liverpool Win The Cup
(To the tune of 'When Johnny Comes Marching Home')

While on the bus to Villa Park, haroo, haroo,
I heard my mate make this remark, haroo, haroo.
We made poor Chelsea weep and ill,
It's Liverpool 2 and Chelsea 0,
And we'll all get blind drunk when Liverpool win the cup.

So here's to Lawrence, Byrne, St John, haroo, haroo,
Milne and Yeats and Stevenson, haroo, haroo.
Hunt and Thompson, what a man,

Lawler, Smith and Callaghan,
And we'll all get blind drunk when Liverpool win the cup.

For the Liverpool lads raise your glass, haroo, haroo.
To Stevenson who made the pass, haroo, haroo.
Thompson had them in a trance,
Bonetti never stood a chance,
And we'll all get blind drunk when Liverpool win the cup.

It's Wembley on the first of May, haroo, haroo,
It's Leeds United labour day, haroo, haroo.
We'll be there to cheer Bill Shankly's side,
And bring the cup to Merseyside,
And we'll all get blind drunk when Liverpool win the cup.

And if it's a draw you'll hear us moan,
Let's use the coin that beat Cologne,
And we'll all get blind drunk when Liverpool win the cup.

*(This song pays tribute to Bill Shankly's 1965 FA Cup winning
side - the first Liverpool FC team to bring the Cup back to
Anfield - with the tune subsequently reused by Kopites for the
Torres Bounce)*

Who Do You Think You Are Kidding Mr Catterick

*(To the Dad's Army theme tune of 'Who Do You Think You Are
Kidding Mr Hitler')*

Who do you think you're kidding Harry Catterick,
If you think the 'Pools no good?

We Have Dreams And Songs To Sing

There's Stevie Heighway, John Toshack
and Chrissy Lawler too,
They scored three goals for Liverpool
and worked it right up you!

So who do you think you are kidding Harry Catterick,
If you think the 'Pools no good?

The Kop was here, they came to cheer,
A famous victory.
With Alun Evans, Tommy Smith,
And our leader Bill Shankly.

So who do you think you are kidding Harry Catterick,
If you think the 'Pools no good?

Well the Everton supporters they have
had quite just enough,
They'd seen their team two goals in front,
Then Shankly called his bluff, 1-2-3.

So who do you think you're kidding Harry Catterick,
If you think the 'Pools no good.

*(Kopites remind then Everton boss Harry Catterick of the Reds' 3-2 derby
victory at Anfield in November 1970)*

Why Are We So Good?
(To the tune of Yorkshire folk song 'Ilkley Moor Baht 'At')

Oh why are we so GOOD?
Oh why are we so GOOD?
Oh why are we so GOOD?
Because we're Liverpool,
Because we're Liverpool,
Because we're Liverpool.

Win The European Cup For Me
(To the tune 'Save Your Love' by Renee & Renato)

Win the European Cup for me,
Wembley, Paris – twice in Italy.
In Istanbul we kept the cup,
Sixth time in Rome let's lift it up.
Win the European cup for me.
Na na na na na...

(Written during the 2008/09 season when Kopites were hoping Rafa Benitez's side might reach a third European Cup final in Roma's Stadio Olimpico, but the Reds were knocked out in the quarter-finals)

You'll Never Walk Alone

Written by Rodgers and Hammerstein for the 1945 Broadway musical 'Carousel', Gerry Marsden and his Pacemakers performed the song in Liverpool clubs during the birth of Merseybeat. Released in October 1963, YNWA – or 'the Liverpool FC song' as the world knows it – was the Pacemakers' third consecutive number one and nowhere was it more popular than on the Kop, as fans sang along with the PA before matches. When it fell from the top spot, Kopites continued to sing it and YNWA has been played and sung at Anfield ever since. It captures the very essence and unity of LFC and remains a source of comfort to those affected by the tragic events that have hit our Club.

You'll Never Walk Alone

When you walk through a storm,
Hold your head up high,
And don't be afraid of the dark.
At the end of a storm,
There's a golden sky,
And the sweet silver song of the lark.

Walk on through the wind,
Walk on through the rain,
Though your dreams be tossed and blown.
Walk on, walk on, with hope in your heart,
And you'll never walk alone,
You'll never walk alone.

Walk on, walk on,
With hope in your heart,
And you'll never walk alone,
You'll never walk alone.

© Imogen Publishing

You're So Original

You're so original,
You're so original…

*(Sung to the same tune and in response to the boring 'sit down Pinocchio'
chant aimed at Phil Thompson by visiting fans when he was assistant
manager)*

You're Supposed To Let Us Win

You're supposed to,
You're supposed to,
You're supposed to let us win,
You're supposed to let us win.

*(Sung to Norwich City when they were leading 1-0 in the final game played
in front of the standing Spion Kop in 1994)*

Song Index

A

- Anfield Wig Walk
- Arbeloa
- Aye-aye Sami

B

- Benny Is A Dancer
- Best Midfield In The World
- Big Ron Yeats
- Bill Shankly From Glenbuck
- Billy Liddell
- Billy The King
- Biscan In Our Club
- Bjornebye In My Gang
- Blame It On Traore
- Blaydon Races
- Bobby Firmino
- Bolo, Bolo Bolo
- Born Under A Liver Bird
- Brendan Rodgers' Liverpool
- Bring On Yer Internazionale
- Brucie Grobbelaar

C

- Champions League, We're Having Kebabs
- Cheyrou
- Come On You Mighty Reds
- Corners Of Europe
- Coutinho-o-o!

D

- Danny, Danny Ings
- Daniel Sturridge
- David Ngog
- Daylight Come And I Wanna Go Home
- Didi Hamann
- Diouf, Diouf, Diouf
- Diouf Is On Fire
- Dirk Kuyt Ole Ole
- Do, Do, Do (Javier Mascherano)
- Dom Dom Solanke
- Doo Wah Didi, Didi

E

- Ee-aye-addio
- Emre Can
- Every Other Saturday

F

- Fernando
- Fields Of Anfield Road
- Five European Cups
- Five Times
- Forza Liverpool
- Fowler's Prayer

G

- Gary Mac
- Gary Macca
- Gathering Cups In May
- Gerard, Gerard Houllier
- Gini Wijnaldum
- Going Loco With Momo Sissoko
- Good King Wenceslas

H

- Hamann, Hamann
- Happiness
- Happy Birthday
- Harry Kewell
- He Ain't Heavy, He's My Brother
- Henchoz
- He's...
...Carragher
...Erik Meijer
...Gary Mac
...Igor Biscan
...Nigel Clough
...Peter Crouch
...Robbie Keane
...Sammy Lee
...Sander Westerveld
...Vladimir Smicer
- He's Alberto Aquilani
- He's Winning Five-One

The Anfield Songbook

- Here's To You
- Hey Big Didi
- Hills Of Anfield
- His First Name Is Lucas
- His Name Is Colin Pascoe
- Hou Let The Reds Out?
- Houllier, Houllier

I

- Ian Rush
- Igor Biscan's Our Hero
- In Dublin's Fair City
- Istanbul
- Istanbul 05
- Istanbul Is Wonderful
- It's A Long Way To Wembley Stadium
- It's Only On Loan

J

- Jari Litmanen
- Jari's All You Need
- Javier Mascherano
- Jerzy Dudek In Our Goal
- Jesus Fernandez Suso
- Jimmy Plaice
- John Arne Riise (I)
- John Arne Riise (II)
- John Houlding

- Johnny Barnes (I)
- Johnny Barnes (II)
- Johnny Barnes Went That Way
- Johnny On The Ball
- Jon Flanagan
- Jordan Henderson
- Jose Enrique
- Josemi
- Jürgen Klopp
- Just Can't Get Enough
- Justice For The 96

K

- Keane For A Fiesta
- Kenny D, The Pride Of Liverpool
- Kuyt Fever
- Kuyt, Kuyt, Let It All Out

L

- La Rafa
- Libpool, Libpool
- Lisha, Lisha
- L-I-V
- Liver Bird Upon My Chest
- Liiiv-er-poool
- Li-ver-pool, Li-ver-pool La La La
- Liv-er-pool (I)
- Liv-er-pool (II)

- Liverpool [Clap, Clap, Clap]
- Liverpool Are Magic
- Liverpool, Liverpool, Liverpool
- Liverpool Will Marmalise Milan
- Liverpool (We're Never Gonna Stop)
- London Bridge Is Falling Down
- Look Out Wembley Here We Come
- Lucas Leiva!
- Luis Garcia

M

- Made For Shooting
- Mane, Mane
- Mario Fantastico
- Mark Gonzalez
- Markus Babbel
- Matchstick Men
- Maxi
- McManaman!
- Men Of Anfield
- Merry Christmas, Everton
- Michael Owen
- Mickey Marsh
- Milan Baros
- Mo Mo Salah
- Mo Oh Salah
- Mo Sissoko
- Mor, Mor, Mor
- Morientes (500 Miles)
- My Liverpool

N

- Nathaniel Clyne
- Neil Mellor

O

- O Come All Ye Faithful
- Oh Campione
- Oh Kyrgiakos
- Oh Liverpool Bill
- Oh Ronny Ronny
- Oh Sami Sami
- Oh Stanley Stanley
- Oh When The Reds Go Marching In
- Oh Yossi Yossi
- One Song
- One-Nil Down, Two-One Up
- Our Mighty Emlyn
- Over The Hills And Far Away

P

- Pass And Move (It's The Liverpool Groove)
- Patrik Berger
- Pepe Reina!
- Phil Babb
- Poor Scouser Tommy
- Put Your Hands Up For Dirk Kuyt

R

- Rafa, Rafael
- Rafa's Got His Dirk Out
- Raul the Red
- Ray Ray Kennedy
- Red And White Kop
- Reds Never Tire
- Ring Of Fire
- Robbie Fowler
- Robbie Keane
- Rockin' Around With Stevie G
- Roma
- Romeo And Juliet

S

- Said Bertie Mee
- Sakho, Sakho!
- Sami Hyypia
- Saturday Night
- Scouser In Gay Paree
- Scousers Rule
- Shankly's Dream
- Show Them The Way To Go Home
- Side By Side
- Sitting On Top Of The World
- Spackman
- Stayed On The Telly
- Ste Gerrard
- Steve Finnan

- Steve Heighway
- Stevie G (I)
- Stevie G (II)
- Steven Gerrard Is Our Captain
- Super Dan
- Sweet Carroll Nine
- Sweet Sixteen

- Team Of Carraghers
- Teddy Bears' Piechnik
- Tell Me Ma
- Thank You Very Much
- Thanks To The Shanks
- That Night In Istanbul
- The Ballad Of Istanbul
- The Best Centre Forward's Wearing Red
- The Boys Of LFC
- The Green, Green Grass Of Anfield
- The Famous Kopites
- The Liverbird Of Liverpool FC
- The McAteer
- The Monster Masch
- The Pride Of Merseyside (I)
- The Pride Of Merseyside (II)
- The Reds are Coming up the Hill
- The Scarf My Father Wore
- The Torres Bounce
- There's A Man From France
- There's Only One Freddie Boswell
- These Reds Are Your Reds

The Anfield Songbook

- This Could Be
- Three Little Birds
- Times They Are A-Changin'
- Titi Camara
- Tommy Mascherano
- Too Good To Be True
- Twelve Days Of Christmas

U

- Underneath The Floodlights

V

- Vladi Smicer

W

- We Are Liverpool (Tra La La La La)
- We Are The Pride Of All Europe
- We Can Do It
- We Love You Liverpool, We Do
- We Shall Not Be Moved
- We Three Kings
- We Won It Five Times
- We'll Be Coming
- Wem-ber-lee, Wem-ber-lee
- Wembley's Our Second Home

- We're A Happy Band
- We're Gonna Win The League
- We're On The March
- We're The Best Behaved Supporters In The Land
- We're The Pride Of Merseyside
- We've Got A Big Pole In Our Goal
- We've Got That Ronnie Whelan
- What A Waste Of Money
- When Liverpool Win The Cup
- Who Do You Think You Are Kidding Mr Catterick
- Why Are We So Good?
- Win The European Cup For Me

Y

- You'll Never Walk Alone
- You're So Original
- You're Supposed To Let Us Win

66 I'm just one of the people who stands on the Kop. They think the same as I do, and I think the same as they do. It's a kind of marriage of people who like each other **99**

Bill Shankly

YOU'LL NEVER WALK ALONE

LIVERPOOL
FOOTBALL CLUB

EST·1892 ®

THE
ANFIELD
SONGBOOK
WE HAVE DREAMS AND SONGS TO SING